FIRST PERFORMANCE

First Performance

Plays for the Junior High School Age

SELECTED AND EDITED BY

Nora MacAlvay & Virginia Lee Comer

HARCOURT, BRACE AND COMPANY · NEW YORK

812.08 — M114

TO CHARLOTTE B. CHORPENNING

"In the hearts of the children are
born the fates of men—and nations."
King Midas and the Golden Touch

FOREWORD

The increasing awareness among educators that theatre is a powerful force in the development of children and young people has emphasized the lack of good plays, and particularly ones which appeal to the junior high school age. Calls for help from librarians and educators led us on an exciting, but often frustrating, search for plays which would hold the interest of directors, be worthy of the efforts of the children involved, and provide good audience fare. Of the many scripts considered, we believe the plays selected most nearly satisfy the standards of sound drama adapted to certain needs of the child at this particular age.

When the junior high school age is reached, the spontaneous creative expression of early childhood is waning and there is a growing desire to emulate adult techniques. The desire to be in a grown-up production for an audience calls for plays which provide real theatre through the scripts themselves and their production possibilities. But in addition, these plays—for first performance—must have qualities which keep the imagination alive and active, and which encourage a creative approach to direction, playing and production. We believe the plays in this collection are a challenge to this age, and are yet within the capacities of this group to present in satisfactory performance.

Boys and girls at this stage of development have an increasing awareness of their own life problems. Plays, even when removed in time and place, give them the satisfaction of participating in relevant problems worked through to a resolution. The themes of the plays we have chosen are basic: for example, the need to belong, as shown in *Papa Pompino and the Prizefighter*; the urge to express one's belief in spite of all obstacles, as in Titian's story; the triumph of freedom over fear as symbolized in *The Secret of the Worn-Out Shoes*. Since groups of a like age are not of uniform maturity level, the plays were selected to allow for differences in this respect. However, as story is still universally of paramount interest, it was essential to choose only those plays in which theme is developed through strong plot.

To children of this age confronted with new and expanding human relationships, drama gives the opportunity to identify emotionally with a character and to experience that character's relationships to those in conflict with him and to those with whom he relates sympathetically. The characters in these plays are within the comprehension of the players. They advance beyond the two dimensional figures of earlier childhood playacting but stop short of the psychological intricacies present in adult drama. The plays offer many significant experiences in human relations, as within the family of *The Utah Trail*; in the sharp contrast of the relationships of Tiziano and Salvatore to their younger sisters in *Titian*; in the changing attitudes of the children to Humpty in *Papa Pompino*; in the father-son relationship of *The Think Machine*.

Children at this period benefit from dynamic group activities and, since the theatre is an intricate organism intermeshing many different aptitudes and interests, producing a play can be a rewarding experience which demonstrates the interdependence of people in reaching a social goal. A play brings together many types of personalities: the doer, the researcher, the planner, the manager, those who seek expression through design, all of whom must work together toward the final production for the enjoyment of the audience. The plays of this collection have colorful backgrounds and allow for full or even elaborate treatment, although each may be very simply done, since they do not rely on the weight or detail of production for their effectiveness. Some require period research, others depend more on imaginative design and several give unusual scope for ingenuity in lighting, music and sound. All are suitable vehicles for production in terms of the group's own resourcefulness.

The junior high school age is a crucial period for children in relation to the theatre, as to any art. It is apt to present the last chance for helping children to know the theatre and to form discriminating tastes before the diverse interests of full adolescence take hold. If they arrive at the junior high school age having never seen plays of a high order especially planned for them and without dramatic experience themselves beyond the stilted assembly skit, their whole future attitude toward drama will be conditioned by what they see and participate in at this age. If they have had a rich experience in theatre going and creative dramatics, they will be even more eager for absorbing plays.

Although these plays have been selected solely on the basis of their suitability for production at the junior high school level, their audience appeal has a wider age range. Theatre groups with adult or mixed age casts playing to young audiences will also find them useful.

Wherever the plays are presented, we hope they will give enjoyment to many children and create a zest for continuing years of theatre experience.

Nora MacAlvay
Virginia Lee Comer

New York City
September, 1951

Contents

xii   Contents

Titian
A DRAMA OF THE RENAISSANCE

BY NORA TULLY

EDITORS' NOTE

Titian, a play based on a legendary incident in the boyhood of the great painter Tiziano Vecelli, later called Titian, captures the vigor, intrigue and dangers of life in the Italian Renaissance. It is the story of a boy who could not resist the urge to express his deepest feelings through painting, even at the risk of punishment. The plot develops the conflict between Tiziano, a cobbler's apprentice, and Salvatore, son of the Lord of the Manor, as the boys enter a competition that will take the winner to Venice to study with the great Bellini. Salvatore's crafty efforts to eliminate Tiziano from the competition are pitted against Tiziano's perseverance in spite of the lack of paints, time and money. The satisfactory resolution stems from this perseverance and Tiziano's acceptance of the help and understanding of his sister, and from the integrity and courage of Bellini and the village priest.

Producing the play is an art experience for players and backstage workers alike. Children today, having many opportunities to use art as a means of expression, will understand Tiziano's desire and will learn, as they work on the play, something of the depth of purpose that is genius and the persistence necessary to its growth. Not only will the play stimulate interest in the life and works of the painter but will lead to research in the customs of the times: the apprentice system in teaching art as well as trades, the meaning of the angelus, the design of costumes and furniture. Even if full production is impossible and the play is done in a classroom or on a curtained platform, such research will be valuable in giving a feeling of the period. Modern experiments in making colored paint from flowers are inconclusive, but whether or not Tiziano actually made fresco paints from mountain flowers is unimportant to the dramatization of this legendary incident. However, experiments made under the guidance of an interested art teacher will arouse the curiosity of young students in the properties and essentials of color and various types of paints.

Titian, produced in a school situation, provides an excellent opportunity for co-operation with art, music and dance departments, or, lacking these, with skilled people of the community.

TITIAN
A Drama of the Renaissance

CHARACTERS

TIZIANO VECELLI, *a boy about 14*

CATARINA VECELLI, *Tiziano's sister, about 11*

LUCIA VECELLI, *Tiziano's mother*

GREGORIO VECELLI, *Tiziano's father*

FATHER ANTON, *a village priest*

SIGNOR ZAMPANTI, *Lord of the Manor*

SALVATORE ZAMPANTI, *his son, about 15*

LISA ZAMPANTI, *sister of Salvatore, about 13*

MARIA ZAMPANTI, *Lady of the Manor*

PEPITA ⎫
CARLOTTA ⎭ *two girls of the village*

SIGNOR BELLINI, *the artist from Venice*

PLACE: *Cadore, Italy*
TIME: *About 1487*

ACT ONE: *The Vecelli kitchen*
Late afternoon

ACT TWO: *An empty house*
Several weeks later

ACT THREE: *The same*
Five minutes later

NOTE ON THE SETTINGS *

The Vecelli kitchen of Act One and the room in the empty
house, background for the rest of the play, may both utilize
the same box set, or both may employ set pieces or screens
on a curtain stage. Essential elements are a fireplace, two doors
and one window. The full sets, or details of units, reflect Italian
medieval architecture for modest dwellings, both houses being
old at the time of the play. Where facilities limit the sets, furniture and properties can carry the flavor of period and locale.

ACT ONE

SCENE: *A medieval Italian kitchen in a modest home in the
village of Cadore. C † back is an open window through
which the mountains can be seen, and in front of which
stands a scoured wooden drop-leaf table. There is a fireplace
stage R, and a door leading to another part of the house UR.
The door to the street is stage L.*

As the curtain opens, SALVATORE *slips quickly in from the
street. He looks back in the direction from which he came
to see if* TIZIANO *is in sight. Then, in a hurry to find a hiding
place from which to spy on* TIZIANO, *he searches the room
quickly, and at the sound of footsteps approaching, ducks
into the doorway R.*

TIZIANO *enters from the street carrying two pairs of shoes
and a small package. Calls, "Catarina." Getting no reply, he
goes to the window and stands an instant looking up at the
mountains. He moves his hand as if drawing their outline on
an imaginary canvas, then moves quickly to the fireplace to*

---

* Full production notes will be found at the end of the play.
  † The following abbreviations are used throughout: C—center
stage; R—right stage; L—left stage; U—upstage; D—downstage.

find a piece of charcoal. *Back at the table, he drops to his knees and begins to sketch the mountains on the drop leaf.* SALVATORE *watches. The angelus rings, and* TIZIANO *rises with bowed head. As soon as the bells cease ringing, he begins to unwrap the package, and* SALVATORE, *in his eagerness to see what the package contains, steals from his hiding place.* TIZIANO *is too absorbed to notice.* SALVATORE *passes behind him to stand UL, openly looking.* TIZIANO, *startled, tries to hide his package.*

TIZIANO. Good day to you, Master Salvatore. I didn't see you come in.

SALVATORE. You were in too great a hurry, Tiziano.

TIZIANO. I wanted to be here to see the mountains while the angelus was ringing.

SALVATORE. What were you doing in Giuseppe's shop?

TIZIANO. I was buying something.

SALVATORE. Only artists like me buy things at Giuseppe's. What could a poor cobbler's apprentice buy there?

TIZIANO. That's not fair, Salvatore. I earned the money I spent. I can't help it that my father isn't a great man like yours.

SALVATORE. Oh, very well. Let me see what it is you've bought. Come on, there's a good fellow.

TIZIANO. Look then. (*He shows the box with little jars of paint.*)

SALVATORE. Paints? (*Laughs.*) What do you want with paints?

TIZIANO. To paint a picture, of course. See our mountains? Aren't they beautiful? I'm going to paint them.

SALVATORE. For the contest?

TIZIANO. Contest? What contest?

SALVATORE (*rclicved*). Of course you wouldn't know about it.

TIZIANO. Tell me, Salvatore. What is this contest? When is it to be? Is it a painting contest? Tell me, please.

SALVATORE. No!

TIZIANO. Don't then. I'll ask someone else. (*Starts to leave.*)

SALVATORE. Wait! What will you give me if I tell you?

TIZIANO. I haven't anything you'd want.

SALVATORE. Let me see. (TIZIANO *takes articles out of a little bag on his belt.*) Give me that. (SALVATORE *grabs a piece of red glass and holds it up to the light.*)

TIZIANO. Not that piece. Red's my favorite color. Take this green. It's pretty.

SALVATORE. I want the red.

TIZIANO. Tell me about the contest, then.

SALVATORE. It's a painting contest, but I don't see what good it will do you to know about it. You couldn't enter it.

TIZIANO. Why not?

SALVATORE. It's only for boys like me who've had lessons, and whose fathers are rich enough to send them to Venice to study.

TIZIANO. To Venice? Where all the real artists are? Isn't that where the great master Bellini lives?

SALVATORE. Yes. It is he who will judge the contest. He will take the winner to Venice with him to be his pupil. Think of that!

TIZIANO (*excited*). To Venice to be his pupil! . . . Are there any rules?

SALVATORE. Yes. One should be sure to do a landscape or something here in Cadore, because the master will want to see if the artist caught the true feeling of his subject.

TIZIANO. You mean, if I should choose to paint the mountains from this window the great Bellini would also have to look from the window before he could award a prize?

SALVATORE. That's it.

TIZIANO (*looking up at the mountains*). I could do it. I know I could.

SALVATORE. I'm not so sure about that. It takes a long time to paint a good picture, and they say the master will be here soon. You couldn't do it. Now I'm all ready for him.

TIZIANO. You're all ready?

SALVATORE. Yes, indeed. My father arranged the contest with the Prince in Venice, and I have my picture done.

TIZIANO. Is it a landscape?

SALVATORE. Well, no. You see, I am a real artist as everyone knows, so I am allowed to choose something different. It's the inside of a room. It is called an interior.

TIZIANO. Your own room in the manor house, is it?

SALVATORE. A room. That's all I'll tell you. You'll see it when I win the contest.

TIZIANO. When did you say the master will come?

SALVATORE. No one knows exactly. About a month from now.

TIZIANO. How I'd like to be the pupil of the great Bellini! Just to paint all day long! All year long . . . always . . . forever!

SALVATORE (*laughs*). Foolish talk! You forget you're only a cobbler's apprentice.

TIZIANO. What difference does that make? Some day I shall paint. You'll see. (SALVATORE *laughs*.) Don't laugh at me. I know I can paint. When I shut my eyes at night I can see pictures on my eyelids. I see mountains and lakes like ours in Cadore. I see the beautiful madonnas in the cathedral. I'd like to paint a madonna now that I have new paints.

SALVATORE. A madonna? (*Laughs.*)

TIZIANO. Yes. I've painted one already on Father Anton's shoe.

SALVATORE. What? On a shoe?

TIZIANO. Yes. (TIZIANO *shows him the shoe that he carried in with him.*) See? It's small though, and I want to make a great big one . . . like those in the cathedral.

SALVATORE. How you talk! Don't you understand that you must have lessons to become an artist? Even I must find a teacher.

TIZIANO. You mean that we are too poor for me to have lessons, so I can never be a painter?

SALVATORE. That's exactly what I mean.

TIZIANO. I see. (SALVATORE *starts looking around the room in a rather rude way.*) Don't you think you should be going home, Salvatore? Won't your father be looking for you? It's nearly suppertime.

SALVATORE. My father told me to wait here for him.

TIZIANO. The Signor is coming here?

SALVATORE. Yes. It's something about the taxes. He's going everywhere. He's changing some of them, I think.

TIZIANO. If he changes ours, I hope he makes them less.

SALVATORE. Oh, yours are hardly anything on this bit of land. It's all worn out. I've heard my father say so. He said it's hardly worth the time he has to spend looking at it. (TIZIANO *takes another bit of charcoal from the fireplace and goes toward the window.*) What are you going to do?

TIZIANO. Aren't our mountains beautiful with the sun on them?

SALVATORE (*standing right in front of the window to see*). Do you really like those old rocks?

TIZIANO. Yes, I do. Don't you?

SALVATORE. No. I like the park from my window much better.

TIZIANO. Stand back, Salvatore. I want to try something. (*He continues the mountain sketching he began earlier on the drop-leaf table.* FATHER ANTON *and* LUCIA VECELLI *appear in the doorway L. As she sees the drawing,* LUCIA *is about to cry out and rush toward her son, but the priest gently pulls her back with his finger on his lips. They watch the boy. As* TIZIANO *reaches for his paints, however,* LUCIA *pulls away and rushes to him.*)

LUCIA. Tiziano! You bad, wicked boy!

TIZIANO. Mother! Father Anton! I've done it at last. So long I've tried to get those jagged rocks just right, and now, there they are like . . . great fingers reaching for heaven!

LUCIA. Oh, you and your rocks with fingers! Get your own fingers busy; wipe that smudge off my table this instant . . . (*Sees* SALVATORE.) Oh, good evening to you, Master Salvatore!

SALVATORE. I'm waiting here for my father. He's coming about the taxes.

LUCIA (*watches* TIZIANO *wiping off the table*). You see how Tiziano is, Father? He should have been delivering your shoes to you, and here he is, playing all afternoon. What am I to do with him?

FATHER A. Nothing, Lucia. Be patient. His love for our hills is no sin. I have felt the beauty in them all my life.

LUCIA. That is all very well for you, Father Anton, but Tiziano is the son of a poor man and must work to help his parents.

FATHER A. Ah, so that is the reason Vecelli has apprenticed the boy to Luigi, the cobbler? I had hoped to see him—

well—a maker of stained glass, perhaps. He loves colors
so. And it's a good trade.

LUCIA. We need shoes. All people need shoes. . . . Tiziano,
where are Father Anton's shoes you were to have de-
livered to him?

TIZIANO. I'm sorry, Father! You see, I started out with your
shoes, but as I came to our house, I thought to run in a
minute to show Catarina my new paints.

FATHER A. And finding her gone, you happened to look out
of the window, and the thought came that now would be
a good time to try our hills.

TIZIANO. Yes . . . but how did you know, Father?

FATHER A. I think I must have been a boy once.

TIZIANO. Father—

FATHER A. Yes, my boy?

TIZIANO. Is it true, that unless one is rich he can never be an
artist?

FATHER A. Whoever put such a thought into your head?

TIZIANO. Salvatore laughed when I said that some day I
would be one. He said that an artist must be taught, and
that my father is too poor to send me to a master.

LUCIA. That he is! Salvatore's father is a rich man.

FATHER A. Many artists have attained fame in spite of poverty.
If you really want to be a great artist, Tiziano, then you
will be willing to face anything in order to become one;
hardships of all kinds, ridicule, and after years of hard
work, perhaps failure.

TIZIANO. I do want to be an artist—more than anything in the
world, Father. And I'd be willing to face anything, too.

FATHER A. (*putting his hand on* TIZIANO's *head*). Bless you,
my boy. I do believe you would.

TIZIANO. There's going to be a contest. Salvatore told me.

But he said that only those who had had lessons could enter. Is that true, Father?

SALVATORE. That's what my father said.

FATHER A. I am certain that the contest is open to all, Tiziano.

TIZIANO. Then there's nothing to keep me from entering now that I have my new paints?

FATHER A. Not that I can see.

TIZIANO. Oh, thank you, Father. (TIZIANO *falls on his knees and grabs the priest's hand.*) I'm sorry about the shoes. Here they are. (TIZIANO *gets one pair of shoes from the table. Not realizing his mistake, he gives* FATHER ANTON *the* SIGNOR'S *shoes.*)

FATHER A. These are very fine-looking shoes, Tiziano. Are you sure they are mine? They look a little large, and a bit too gay for me. (FATHER ANTON *turns the shoes over to see how large the sole is and finds the picture of a red devil painted on one.*) Well—are you quite certain these are mine, Tiziano?

TIZIANO (*thinking* FATHER ANTON *has seen the painting of a madonna which is on his own shoe*). Don't you like them, Father?

FATHER A. The shoes are very well made, but there is a picture on the sole of one that I don't quite understand. Did you do it?

TIZIANO. Yes. I hope you won't mind, Father. I thought of it when I thought of you. (*Shyly.*)

FATHER A. You thought of a wicked red devil when you thought of me?

TIZIANO. What? A devil? Oh, no, Father—there's a mistake. (*Gives him the other pair.*) That was meant for someone else. These are your shoes.

FATHER A. Well, well, this is better. You startled me, young man. But, tell me, do you think any man would want a devil on his shoe?

TIZIANO. I couldn't help it, Father. A red devil is what I saw when I looked at his sole.

LUCIA. Tiziano! What are you saying? What have you done?

TIZIANO. Oh, Mother, wait, I'll show you. Look at the sole of your shoe, Father Anton.

LUCIA. Oh, Tiziano Vecelli!

TIZIANO. You don't mind? (*As* FATHER ANTON *looks at the painting of the madonna.*)

FATHER A. No . . . Of course I don't mind. It was a beautiful thought, Tiziano. But I cannot wear this shoe now, you know, for I could hardly put the Blessed Virgin under my foot.

TIZIANO. Oh, I didn't think of that. Yesterday as I worked on the shoes, the picture of our Lady kept appearing before me on the clean leather. When they were finished, something made me try to paint Her there. (TIZIANO *takes the shoe and puts it on the table.*)

FATHER A. And you must keep Her just as She is. I'll commission you to make a new shoe to match the other.

TIZIANO. Oh, thank you, Father.

LUCIA. You spoil him, Father. (*Turning to* TIZIANO.) Always seeing pictures! Forget your pictures a minute and put some more wood on the fire.

TIZIANO. Yes, Mother—with my new paints, I'll be able to make a more beautiful red than with the cobbler's dye.

LUCIA. New paints! Your father will have something to say about your paints when he hears that you've ruined Father Anton's shoes for walking, and that I caught you about to paint on my nice clean table.

TIZIANO. Oh, Mother, please don't tell Father. He'll be so angry. I didn't mean to be bad. (*A richly dressed man appears in the doorway. It is the* SIGNOR ZAMPANTI.)

ZAMPANTI. Good day to you, Signora Vecelli! Ah, and to you, Father Anton.

LUCIA. Good day to you, Signor.

ZAMPANTI. Is Gregorio about?

LUCIA. He is on the land, Signor. Shall I send for him?

ZAMPANTI. Do you expect him back soon?

LUCIA. Yes, Signor, any time now. It is nearly mealtime.

ZAMPANTI. Then I shall wait for him. (*Sees* FATHER ANTON'S *shoes on the table. Picks them up and examines them.*) Are these shoes from Luigi's?

TIZIANO. Yes, Signor. They are Father Anton's.

ZAMPANTI. Who painted them?

TIZIANO. I did, Signor.

ZAMPANTI. You? (*He examines them more closely, frowning.*) Well, well! (*He picks them up and examines them once more, drops them and moves away.*)

TIZIANO. Does the painting displease you, Signor?

ZAMPANTI. I am surprised that a cobbler's boy should be interested in painting. Such a pastime is for boys like mine.

TIZIANO. Yes, Signor. I see.

ZAMPANTI. Luigi said you had my shoes.

FATHER A. It was my shoes he meant. (*He slips own shoes out of sight, puts* ZAMPANTI'S *shoes under his arm.*) Well, Lucia, I must be on my way. Your neighbor down the road awaits my presence at supper.

LUCIA. Good day then, Father.

FATHER A. Good day, Lucia.

ZAMPANTI (*bows as* FATHER ANTON *leaves;* LUCIA *picks up a water jug and moves toward the street door*). Pray go about your work, Signora. I can take care of myself.

LUCIA. Thank you, Signor Zampanti. I shall walk with Father Anton as far as the well. (*Exits.*)

ZAMPANTI. Tiziano! That is your name, boy?

TIZIANO. Yes, Signor.

ZAMPANTI. Run to meet your father and urge him to come faster. I cannot wait until night for him.

TIZIANO. Yes, Signor. (*Exits.*)

ZAMPANTI. Salvatore, why did you not tell me of this Tiziano Vecelli?

SALVATORE. What of him, Father? You know he is the son of Gregorio and Lucia.

ZAMPANTI. Indeed—but I did not know that he had an interest in painting.

SALVATORE. Oh, he's nobody.

ZAMPANTI. That boy has great ability. Who is his teacher?

SALVATORE. He's had no teaching. They have not money enough.

ZAMPANTI. They have money enough to provide him with paints, however.

SALVATORE. He made the picture on the shoe at Luigi's shop. He's a cobbler's apprentice. But today he bought some paints at Giuseppe's and he says he will enter the contest.

ZAMPANTI (*startled*). He says that, does he? He has talent— great talent—more than you, my son.

SALVATORE. Why—he's just—

ZAMPANTI (*growing excited*). I can't have your chances ruined. You must win this contest. You must go to Venice. You shall become the favorite of the Prince as soon as you are old enough. My great name shall be carried on through

your works. That is my plan, but this Vecelli boy is likely
to spoil it. He must be stopped, do you hear?

SALVATORE. Yes, Father. But how?

ZAMPANTI. Have these Vecellis any money at all?

SALVATORE. I heard Lucia say that it was because they are
poor that Tiziano is apprenticed to a cobbler.

ZAMPANTI. Ah! I have it. Vecelli's taxes shall be raised. I'll
tell him it is the law because his land is rich. He will not
blame me. I shall be very sorry.

SALVATORE. How will that stop Tiziano, Father?

ZAMPANTI. He will have to work all the time, and turn over
every penny to his father to help pay the taxes. (Very
pleased with himself.)

SALVATORE. But he has paints, and he'll find time to make a
picture somehow. He is determined to enter the contest.

ZAMPANTI. His paints must be got rid of. You've got to win
this contest. You are too young to understand fully, Salvatore. There is another who would like to rule in my place.
He has spies, Salvatore, lurking about to trap me in some
failure or wrong-doing. They seek information to give the
Prince that will overthrow the Zampantis.

SALVATORE. I wish I were grown up.

ZAMPANTI. If you win this contest, you will live with the
Prince—paint in his court—

SALVATORE. It will be easy for me to win.

ZAMPANTI. Then, because of you, he will protect me. Do
you understand?

SALVATORE. Yes, Father. I'll win.

ZAMPANTI. My son, you've never done anything as good as
Tiziano's little painting.

SALVATORE. But you haven't seen mine yet. Do you remember that old empty house at the edge of the village? Well,

I've done a painting of the corner of the main room. Just wait until Bellini sees it. It will win—

ZAMPANTI. Hush! (LUCIA *enters with water.*)

LUCIA. Has Gregorio not arrived yet, Signor?

TIZIANO (*following on her heels*). Father sent me ahead to say that he will be here soon, Signor.

ZAMPANTI. Can't wait! Can't wait! But I will come back later. (*Hands a doublet which he carries over his arm to* TIZIANO.) Mend this doublet while I'm gone. Come, Salvatore.

LUCIA (*following the* ZAMPANTIS *to the door*). Oh, Signor, I do hope our taxes will be lowered this year. Times are very bad with us.

ZAMPANTI. My good woman, don't worry yourself about the taxes. Good evening. I shall be back. (*Exits with* SALVATORE. TIZIANO *sits at the table sewing the doublet.*)

LUCIA. It is too bad to make the Signor come back.

TIZIANO. I'm glad they're gone—both of them.

LUCIA. Tiziano! You mustn't say such things. The Signor is a good man and Salvatore is his son.

TIZIANO (*taking up a paint brush*). I don't think he's a good man.

LUCIA. Tiziano!

TIZIANO. Well, I don't. (*He paints a red devil on the back of the doublet as he talks. This can be painted previously and concealed from the audience so that* TIZIANO *can fake painting.*) I—I just don't. He makes me feel—I don't know —he makes me— Oh, I know he's not a good man. (*Sound of faint singing off.*)

LUCIA. Tiziano! (*Singing grows louder.*) That will be Catarina now. It's about time she came to help with the supper. (*Exits on business of getting supper. Enter* CATARINA, LISA,

PEPITA *and* CARLOTTA. *They carry flowers; one has a garland, another a wreath in her hair.)*

CATARINA. Oh—there you are, brother!

LISA. Why didn't you come to the inn to help make garlands for the flower festival?

PEPITA. Yes, why didn't you? It was such fun!

TIZIANO. Were there many helping?

CARLOTTA. Oh, yes! Almost everyone!

CATARINA. Even Salvatore for a while.

LISA. Yes, even my brother. Did you know that if he wins the painting contest, he's going to Venice? My father arranged the contest himself.

CATARINA. And he'll have a grand send-off with flowers and music and dancing.

TIZIANO. I'm going to enter the contest. (GIRLS *laugh at the idea.)*

CATARINA. You'd like to go to Venice and have all the girls throw flowers at your feet, wouldn't you? Well, I'll throw them now. (CATARINA *tosses flowers to him at table.* OTHERS *pelt him, too, teasing.* CATARINA *gets a glimpse of the painting on the doublet.)* Oh—what have you been painting, Tiziano? *(She snatches the doublet.* TIZIANO *chases her to retrieve it. She eludes him and holds doublet so that* GIRLS *and audience see the devil on its back.)*

PEPITA. Look! A devil!

LISA. Isn't he a wicked old fellow?

CARLOTTA. He frightens me.

CATARINA. But what is this you've painted it on, Tiziano? Why—it's a good doublet!

TIZIANO. Let me have it! *(He hides it behind him.)*

LUCIA *(entering).* Here—pick up those petals before they

stain the floor! (GIRLS *hasten to obey.*) Good evening, Signorina! (*To* LISA.)

LISA. Good evening to you, Signora Vecelli. (GREGORIO VECELLI *enters.*)

VECELLI. Where is the Signor? Wouldn't he wait?

LUCIA. He'll be back. It's the taxes, Gregorio.

VECELLI (*worried*). If they had been the same, he'd have told you.

LISA. Here's my father now. (ZAMPANTI *appears in the doorway.*)

ZAMPANTI. Well, Lisa! Good evening, Vecelli. (SALVATORE *is with him, joins* GIRLS.)

VECELLI. Good evening, Signor! You wish to see me—about the taxes?

ZAMPANTI. H'm—yes. The taxes. You have a fine piece of land, Gregorio.

VECELLI. Not very fine just now, Signor. It has given everything it has, and I have no money these days to enrich the soil. It is worn out.

ZAMPANTI. Come now. Things can't be as bad as that. I looked the place over to confirm the report of my man. See, here it is. (*Opens scroll.*) Gregorio Vecelli, Class A. That means very good indeed, so I'm afraid that the man who examined the place last time made a mistake if he told you it was not.

VECELLI. There is no better judge of land than I, Signor, and I insist that my land is worn out.

ZAMPANTI. Then if that is so it must be your own fault, my good fellow.

VECELLI. It has been in this condition for years. Now it is hopeless. I cannot make enough off it this year to meet the taxes even if they were reduced.

ZAMPANTI. That is sad indeed, my friend. Then you will have to raise the money elsewhere, for according to this paper the value of your land has greatly increased. Your taxes, therefore, increase this year. Let me see how much—

LUCIA. Increase? Then we are lost.

VECELLI. How much are they increased, Signor?

ZAMPANTI. I am sorry indeed. I wish that it were another's duty to give you such news. Fine people as you are—it grieves me sorely.

VECELLI. I understand, Signor. It is your duty. It cannot be helped. But how much are the taxes increased?

ZAMPANTI. One thousand ducats, my friend.

VECELLI. One thousand! That is outrageous, Signor! How can it be? The land is worthless, I tell you! (*Getting excited.*) Worthless!

LUCIA. Hush, hush, Gregorio! The Signor cannot help that. Perhaps there will be a way to meet this need later.

ZAMPANTI. I should be glad to help you if I could. Let me see—you have a son here?

VECELLI. Tiziano!

ZAMPANTI. Does he work?

VECELLI. Only as an apprentice, half-day. He brings in very little.

ZAMPANTI. To whom is he apprenticed?

VECELLI. To Luigi, the cobbler.

ZAMPANTI. He'll be a cobbler then? That is a fine trade—a sensible trade. Well—I shall speak to Luigi and get him to take Tiziano for the whole day and double his pay.

VECELLI. Ah—that is fine of you, Signor Zampanti.

LUCIA (*falling on her knees and kissing his hand*). You are a good man, Signor. God will reward you.

ZAMPANTI. There, there, my good woman, I only wish there were more I could do. Tiziano, is my doublet ready?

LISA (*gasps*). Oh, it's Father's!

LUCIA. Yes, Signor. Here it is. I hope he did a good piece of work on it, Signor.

ZAMPANTI. So do I. (*He starts to put it on.*)

TIZIANO. Let me help you, Signor.

ZAMPANTI. It's very well done. You will make a good cobbler. (*He stands with back to audience.*)

SALVATORE (*sees picture—laughs*). Oh-h! Look at your doublet!

ZAMPANTI. What do you mean? My doublet!

SALVATORE. There is a devil on your back.

ZAMPANTI. Where?

SALVATORE. On the back of your doublet! Take it off and see!

ZAMPANTI (*takes it off*). Who did this? It's still wet. It was done here.

LUCIA. Oh, Signor! Who would do such a thing!

VECELLI. Surely you're mistaken, Signor! No one in my house would be so bold.

LISA. Yes—he would. Tiziano did it.

LUCIA. Tiziano!

VECELLI. What!

ZAMPANTI. Why, of course, it was you. The priest's shoes—I remember! Vecelli, I was sorry for you before. I am more so now that I know your son.

VECELLI. Signor, Signor, anything I can do to make this right —I'll do. The price of the doublet—that I will try to pay though we go hungry to do it.

ZAMPANTI. How much money have you then? Though money will not wipe out this insult.

VECELLI. 'Twas but a boy's prank, Signor. (*Digging into his pocket.*) Alas, I have but a few pence.

ZAMPANTI. Does not your son get a wage?

VECELLI. Tiziano—you were paid today?

TIZIANO. Yes, Father. (*Hands* VECELLI *two coins.*)

VECELLI. Where is the other piece? You've given me two.

TIZIANO. It is all I have, Father.

VECELLI. What is the meaning of this— Where is that other piece? Did you lose it?

TIZIANO. No, Father, I—I—

VECELLI. You what?

TIZIANO. I spent it.

VECELLI. Spent it? What on earth would you spend it for? Don't we give you everything you need, clothes and food —poor as we are?

TIZIANO. Yes, Father.

VECELLI. Then what *did* you spend it for?

TIZIANO. I've bought something I've always wanted very much.

VECELLI. What?

TIZIANO. I bought some paints.

VECELLI. Paints!

TIZIANO. I'm sorry, Father.

VECELLI. Sorry! A lot of good that will do us now. There is not money enough to pay for the doublet, Signor.

SALVATORE. Father, take what he has and the paints as well. I can use the paints!

ZAMPANTI. A very good idea! That's just what we'll do. Take the paints. (SALVATORE *goes to the table where the paints lie, grabs them right from under* TIZIANO's *nose and laughs.* TIZIANO *buries his head in his arms on the table. He crushes the flower petals in his misery, making great stains*

*on the table and drop leaf where they can be seen by the
audience.)*

VECELLI. Oh, thank you, Signor. You are indeed kind for
letting Tiziano off so easily.

ZAMPANTI. Well—it was a boy's prank, as you say. We'll forget it, and to show that I bear you no ill will, I shall keep
my word about speaking to Luigi. I shall see that he gives
Tiziano work enough to keep him busy all day long.

VECELLI, LUCIA. God bless you, Signor.

ZAMPANTI. Come, Salvatore—Lisa—it grows late. Good night,
my friends. *(They exit. Their laughter is heard outside.)*

LUCIA. Pepita—Carlotta, run home quickly. It is late, your
mothers will be looking for you. Good night.

GIRLS. Good night. *(Exit.)*

VECELLI *(glances at* TIZIANO *crying, and shakes his head).*
That I should have such a son! But perhaps now you'll
learn to be a man, Tiziano, and attend to your work. And
don't let me ever catch you playing with paints again.

LUCIA. This is what comes of all his talk about wanting to be
an artist. It's a pity he's like that. *(She looks at* TIZIANO *and
sees the stains on the table.)* Oh, look you, Tiziano, what
you've done to my nice clean table! Such stains! Scrub
them off this minute, do you hear? *(*CATARINA *goes to get a
cloth.)* Supper will be ready any minute, husband.

VECELLI. What time have I to be thinking of supper? With
not a coin in the house, now? I must find Luigi and see
if he'll advance some money on Tiziano's wages. *(Exits.)*

LUCIA. There's no need to do it now, Gregorio. Have your
supper first. *(Following him to door.)* Gregorio—listen to
me—you'll feel better later— *(She shakes her head and
exits into other part of house.)*

CATARINA. Don't feel so badly, Tiziano. You feel worse about losing an old box of paints than I did when I broke my best doll.

TIZIANO. It's not the same thing, Catarina. Besides you broke the doll yourself. It's different when somebody you don't like takes it from you.

CATARINA. Anyway I didn't just keep on crying. I made a new doll out of my old ones.

TIZIANO. I can't make new paints! And Salvatore just told me that the great master Bellini is coming soon.

CATARINA. Well, is he not still coming?

TIZIANO. Yes, but don't you see? When I heard that he was coming, I planned a picture of the Madonna and our lakes and our mountains to enter in the contest. Now that my paints are gone, what can I do? (*He sobs with head on table.*)

CATARINA. Please, Tiziano. You'd better get these stains off the table before Mother comes back or you'll get into more trouble. I'll help you. (*She takes cloth and begins to scrub. Presently* TIZIANO *looks up and watches her.*) Oh, it won't come off! It stains just like paint!

TIZIANO. Like paint? Here let me try. (*He scrubs harder and harder.*) It stains like paint! It stains like paint! It is paint!

CATARINA. Oh, dear! Scrub harder then. (*The stains remain.*) Never mind, Tiziano, maybe Mother won't notice them.

TIZIANO. Never mind? But I do mind. I do. (*He grabs* CATARINA *and dances about the room.*) Oh, Rina, I shall paint a picture after all, and I'll go to Venice to the great Bellini. I shall go to Venice—

CATARINA. Stop, you silly! I'm all out of breath. Paint a picture without paints? Go to Venice without money? How you do talk!

TIZIANO. No, wait a minute. (*He picks up* CATARINA *and lifts her to the table. He grabs a shawl for her head, places a doll in her arms, picks up flowers from the floor, and drops on his knees before her, offering flowers to the doll.*) Sing the Madonna song. (CATARINA *sings lullaby.*)

CATARINA (*softly*). Whatever has come over you, Tiziano? Are you gone mad?

TIZIANO. No! Listen. I shall paint a picture of the Blessed Virgin with the child in her arms and a boy like me offering flowers to the Babe. It has been in my heart to do it for a long time.

CATARINA. But how, Tiziano, without any paints?

TIZIANO. I said I couldn't make new paints, didn't I?

CATARINA. Yes.

TIZIANO. I can make them. Look at these stains—red, yellow, blue, green—Catarina, don't you see? I need no more than the juices of these flowers. God has given me paints!

CATARINA. But how long it will take! How can you ever get enough color from the flowers before they're all gone?

TIZIANO. You must help me, Rina. Say you will.

CATARINA. Yes, I'll help you. But how?

TIZIANO. You can gather flowers for me.

CATARINA. So I can. I love to do that anyway. But, oh, Tiziano, Father will never let you do it.

TIZIANO. He mustn't know what I'm doing, Catarina. He'd destroy the picture if he found it.

CATARINA. How will you keep him from knowing?

TIZIANO. I'll paint it in our old empty house at the edge of the village.

CATARINA. In that lonely place?

TIZIANO. Why not? It's just an old house that nobody wants any more. It would be a good place.

CATARINA. But what will you do for a canvas?

TIZIANO. I shan't need any. There's a place on the wall just made for my picture.

CATARINA. Isn't it exciting? Cadore will be very proud of you.

TIZIANO. Now, Catarina, listen. Nobody must know what we're doing. Do you hear?

CATARINA. Oh, can't I tell even Lisa? Her brother's going to be in it, too.

TIZIANO. Oh, no! She'd tell Salvatore and—well, I don't trust him. You mustn't tell anybody. Father would be sure to find out.

CATARINA. I won't tell, Tiziano.

TIZIANO (*leads her over to a crucifix on the wall*). That isn't enough. Here, touch the cross and promise.

CATARINA. But isn't it wicked to do this when Father doesn't want you to paint?

TIZIANO. He'd want me to paint if he only knew how much it meant to me, but there's no way to make him know, Catarina. I'd ask him for his permission, but I don't dare.

CATARINA. Yes. He's too angry now about the money.

TIZIANO. It can't be wicked to want to paint the Madonna. Besides, I must do it. I feel it here. (*He places his hand on his heart.*)

CATARINA. I'll do it. (*She touches the cross.*) I, Catarina, promise to tell no one that Tiziano Vecelli is painting a picture on the wall of the old house, or that I, Catarina, his sister, am helping him to go to Venice to be a great painter.

CURTAIN

ACT TWO

SCENE: *The main room of an empty house. The same set as in Act One may be used—stripped, except that in place of the fireplace should be a large window with a bench under it. On the back wall is the painting already covered with a cloth painted to match the walls. This painting is kept covered until the end of the play. There is a door L as in Act One, this time leading to another room. The door R leads outside. A large empty wine cask stands DR on a platform about 8 ins. high. In front of the painting is a bench or a plank resting on two small kegs. A brazier is DL and a small cask UR. On the platform are large glass jars of bright colored paint (water color): blue, yellow, red (almost gone), green.*

TIZIANO *stands on bench before covered painting on the back wall, at curtain rise. He holds back one corner of the canvas as he puts on the last stroke. Jumps down happily. Runs to the brazier, blows on the fire and pours water into the pan on it. Runs to the window, opens it and calls:*

TIZIANO. Catarina! Catarina!

CATARINA (*off in the distance*). I'm coming.

TIZIANO. Hurry, then! I've something to tell you. (*He goes back to his picture, but growing impatient starts for the window again.*) Catarina! (*Reaches the window just as* CATARINA *does.*)

CATARINA. Boo! (*Mimicking.*) May I really come in today?

TIZIANO. If you promise not to look at the picture.

CATARINA. Not till you say I may. (TIZIANO *opens the door.* CATARINA *enters.*)

TIZIANO. Rina! (*He grabs her and pulls her toward the empty barrel. They both sit.*) Guess what?

CATARINA. Oh—I can't.

TIZIANO. Try!

CATARINA. Well then, is it good or bad?

TIZIANO. Not bad.

CATARINA. Then it's good—and it must be— Oh, Tiziano, is it?

TIZIANO. Yes, it's finished! And just in time. The great Bellini is judging the pictures today.

CATARINA. And yours is ready for him.

TIZIANO. And he'll like it.

CATARINA. And you'll win the contest.

TIZIANO. And go to Venice to study.

CATARINA. Oh, Tiziano! But what about the contest? How long will the master judge the pictures?

TIZIANO. Until sundown.

CATARINA. And when will he see yours? How will he know about it? Will you go for him or have you already told him? Did you see him yourself?

TIZIANO. Wait a minute. No, I haven't seen him yet, and he doesn't know about my picture. He'll see mine when the sun is going down and the angelus is ringing. I thought you would like to go for him when I've finished cleaning up.

CATARINA. Oh, yes, I would. How will the judging be done? I mean where?

TIZIANO. Each one will show his painting where he made it. That way the master will know if it is a good likeness. After he has seen them all he will go to the village hall to make it known who the winner is. See?

CATARINA. Yes, Tiziano. I wish I could see your picture now. Can't I? Just one little peek? (TIZIANO, *taking a brush, disappears behind the cover.*) Oh—you have it covered and it looks just like the wall.

TIZIANO. Of course it does. I painted it that way so that people passing the window would think it was the wall.

CATARINA. That was a good idea. What are you doing? I thought it was finished.

TIZIANO. It is.

CATARINA. Then what are you doing to it?

TIZIANO. Signing my name. (*Spells.*) T-i-z-i-a-n-o V-e-c-e-l-l-i.

CATARINA (*leaning farther, trying to see behind the cover*). Oh, what is that beautiful red? The Madonna's robe?

TIZIANO (*threateningly*). Rina!

CATARINA. And the lovely blue? And the yellow so bright— that must be the Christ Child's hair.

TIZIANO (*pulling her away*). Now, Catarina, that's not fair. You said you wouldn't look if I let you come in. Now you must go.

CATARINA. First I'll help you throw all the paint things away.

TIZIANO. No! No! There's still some powdered poppies. I'm going to make it into paint. The red is almost gone.

CATARINA. What for?

TIZIANO. I'll be needing it.

CATARINA. Are you going to paint another picture, Tiziano?

TIZIANO. Another? I shall paint hundreds of them. I'm going to start another tomorrow. Help me now.

CATARINA. Oh, yes. (*Both cross to the brazier.*)

TIZIANO. The water's hot. You pour in the flower powder. I'll stir.

CATARINA. There are a lot of petals still.

TIZIANO. Powder them right into the hot water.

CATARINA. Nobody would think these were ever flowers.

TIZIANO (*snatches flowers from her hair*). Here are some more!

CATARINA. Oh, those are fresh.

TIZIANO. The color will soak out anyway. (CATARINA *starts to put leaves in too.*) Oh, here! Don't put in any green. That'll dull the red! I'll pull off the petals.

CATARINA. Here's a little bluebell left. Shall I throw it away?

TIZIANO. No—put it in. It will make the red more beautiful.

CATARINA. You know, it always made me sad before to gather flowers and see them die. Now when the lovely petals wither I know they aren't dead at all.

TIZIANO. No? It seems to me that just today when the last bunch of yellow crocuses went into the hot water I saw tears in somebody's eyes. What about it, Rina?

CATARINA. But when I saw the gold come out of them, I didn't mind any more that they died.

TIZIANO (*runs to the painting and pulls back cover enough to show the Christ Child's head*). Died! Look!

CATARINA. They're alive! They're alive! They aren't dead at all, Tiziano!

TIZIANO. They're the gold of the Christ Child's hair.

CATARINA. It's wonderful, isn't it? They'll live as long as your picture stays on that wall.

TIZIANO. They'll live as long as I can remember it. (*Street music in distance.* TIZIANO *and* CATARINA *dance for joy.*)

CATARINA. Now is it ready for the glue?

TIZIANO (*tries the mixture on the brazier*). No, it's still too hot to pour. While it cools, help me put things away. (*They carry jars of paint—except red—into the other room, so that everything to do with the painting is out of sight, except the brazier and the jar for the red paint, and one with glue.)* Bring a jar now and we'll see what it's like.

CATARINA. Tiziano, let me pour it this time?

TIZIANO. Be careful, then. It wobbles.

CATARINA. I will.

TIZIANO. The handle may be hot—look out!

CATARINA *(the handle is hot and she jerks, spilling some of the paint on the floor).* Oh! Oh!

TIZIANO. Oh, Catarina—you've spilled some of my precious red and the poppies are almost gone.

CATARINA. I'm sorry, Tiziano. The handle was hot. You told me too late. I'll hold the jar. You pour it. *(TIZIANO pours the red paint into a glass jar.)* It's lovely, Tiziano.

TIZIANO *(taking paint to window).* Mm, but see it here with the light shining through it. I believe it's even nicer than my other red.

CATARINA. Maybe my bluebell did it. Now is it ready for the glue?

TIZIANO. Yes. Do you think you could put it in?

CATARINA. Yes, let me.

TIZIANO. Be careful then. I'll put the brazier away. *(He takes it to storeroom.)*

CATARINA. May I help you always like this?

TIZIANO. Yes, of course, if I'm here, but you forget I'm going to Venice.

CATARINA. Won't you ever come back again?

TIZIANO. I shall always come back to the mountains. I'm sure there can't be any in the whole world more beautiful. *(He looks out of window.)*

CATARINA. You put them in your picture, didn't you?

TIZIANO. Yes, and I shall put them in ever so many more.

CATARINA. I saw Tonio's picture.

TIZIANO. What is it?

CATARINA. Some trees and goats and things. It isn't very good.

TIZIANO. Have you seen Salvatore's?

CATARINA. No, he won't let anyone see it, but I know what it is. His sister Lisa told me.

TIZIANO. He should have made her promise, the way I did you. What is the picture? A room in a house? An interior?

CATARINA. Yes, that's what it is—a room in an old house, she said. Wouldn't it be funny if it were in this one? But of course it couldn't be.

TIZIANO. It could be this one, you know, for his picture has been done a long time. He told me that it was finished the day he took my paints.

CATARINA. Then it would be funny indeed. Because, don't you see, it couldn't be right now with your picture on the wall. (*Both laugh.*)

TIZIANO. Now I'm ready for the master. How does it look?

CATARINA. Can't we get the stains off the floor?

TIZIANO. They *don't* look very nice. The master will think I'm a careless sort of person. I know, I'll move the cask over them, then they can't be seen. (*He moves barrel from stage R to cover red stain on floor.*)

CATARINA. It looks a little bare, doesn't it?

TIZIANO. Yes, I wish I could have taken my picture outside where there are flowers and birds singing and people.

CATARINA. Well, we can bring flowers inside, can't we?

TIZIANO. Of course we can. Let's get more quickly and you can help me put them about. You've been a great help to me, Rina, gathering all the flowers I've needed. I don't think there are many boys in Cadore whose sisters would want to help them as you have.

CATARINA. It's fun. Besides, I learned a lot.

TIZIANO. What did you learn?

CATARINA. Well, I learned which flowers make the best colors. Pink primroses, bluebells, yellow crocuses, and scarlet poppies. And I learned how many it takes just to make a tiny bit of paint.

TIZIANO. Very good, Rina.

CATARINA. Flowers do make lovely colors but it takes a long time. It would be easier if we had money to buy the paints already made.

TIZIANO. Of course it takes a long time, and having to work so hard for Luigi, I needed every spare minute to mix the colors and to paint. So now you see I couldn't have done it without you and you shall have your reward when I go to Venice.

CATARINA. A reward, Tiziano?

TIZIANO. Yes, let me see! I shall send you a red silk dress!

CATARINA. Oh, to wear at a festival! How nice!

TIZIANO. And a string of pearls, real ones!

CATARINA. Just like Lisa's!

TIZIANO. And let me think, what else—

CATARINA. Oh, nothing else, Tiziano. There won't be money enough.

TIZIANO. You forget, I'll be rich when I go to Venice. I know what else—a fine box of bon-bons. (*He moves the small cask for the fresh flowers to one side of his picture.*)

CATARINA. And you can have some of them. Now let's hurry for the flowers. (*She jumps down from the window seat.* TIZIANO *looks about, then runs to the storeroom door and locks it.*) Come on, Tiziano.

TIZIANO. I'll hide the key to the storeroom. Go ahead. (CATARINA *exits. He puts the key on a little ledge or a nail near*

*the door where it is out of sight. Goes out and locks door
behind him, but forgets to shut window. Two heads appear in the window almost immediately. They are* SALVA-
TORE *and* LISA.)

LISA. Is this the place?

SALVATORE. Yes. Come on, let's go in. (*They go to the door
and find it locked, then appear at the window again.*)

LISA. Now what are you going to do?

SALVATORE. Climb in the window, of course. (*He climbs in.*)

LISA. What about me?

SALVATORE. Can't you climb in, too?

LISA. Not by myself. Come and help me.

SALVATORE. Girls are a nuisance. (*He helps her in.*)

LISA. Was the door locked before? Did you always have to
come in the window?

SALVATORE. No, it wasn't locked. Someone's been here since
I was in last time. It was all dirty then and now it's clean.

LISA. Come on, then. Let me see your painting. I'm getting
tired of hearing about the old thing. (SALVATORE *hands her
the picture.*)

SALVATORE. There! What do you think of it?

LISA. Not bad! Yes, there's the door and the cask. It looks
all right to me, Salvatore. (*She hands it back to him and
he studies it, while* LISA *goes to the little door, L.*) What's
in here?

SALVATORE. A storeroom and the back door of the house.

LISA (*tries the door*). It's locked, and there isn't any key.

SALVATORE (*looking at the cask*). Yes, there is a key. It was in
the door the last time I saw it.

LISA. Then where is it now? It isn't here. There must be
something precious hidden in there, or why would the
door be locked?

SALVATORE. That's silly!

LISA. Is it silly? Wasn't the front door locked, too, and you said yourself that someone's been here.

SALVATORE (*leaning on the cask as if he were about to lift it*). That's true.

LISA. What's wrong with you? What are you trying to do to the cask?

SALVATORE. It's in the wrong place. It's been pushed over here and it should be over there. Help me to move it back to match the picture.

LISA. Move it yourself, lazy.

SALVATORE. Now, Lisa! All right then, you look at the picture while I move it and tell me when I've got it right. (LISA *takes the picture.*) How's that? (*As he moves cask.*)

LISA. No, a little more to the right.

SALVATORE (*moving to the left*). Is this right then?

LISA. No. That's the wrong way. I said right, not left.

SALVATORE. This is right!

LISA. Don't you know which is your right hand?

SALVATORE. This one? (*Indicating right hand.*)

LISA. Yes, stupid!

SALVATORE (*moving cask to the right*). Now is it right?

LISA. Yes. Oh, look there on the floor where the cask was standing. (*Points to stains made by the spilled paint.*)

SALVATORE. What is it?

LISA. Look and see. What does it feel like?

SALVATORE (*stooping and running his hand over the stain*). I can't tell what it is because it's soaked into the wood.

LISA. It's red enough—whatever it is. What could it be— something red and runny enough to soak into wood. . . .

SALVATORE. Do you suppose it's blood?

LISA. Oh-h-h—

SALVATORE. Do you suppose there's been a murder?

LISA. In here?

SALVATORE. Yes. (*Backs toward wall near door and knocks down key.*) Oh, what was that?

LISA. The key. Look!

SALVATORE. The storeroom key! Something funny's been going on here.

LISA. You aren't afraid! (SALVATORE *fiddles around with the lock.*) Then why don't you open the door?

SALVATORE. The key sticks.

LISA. Here, let me try it. (*Turns the key.*) There! (SALVATORE *hesitates.*) Why don't you go in? (*He peeks in fearfully. Just as he is about to enter* LISA *says "Boo."*)

SALVATORE (*jumping*). Lisa! Don't do that. (*Enters.*) The place is full of paint.

LISA. Paint!

SALVATORE. Yes—blue, green, yellow and red. (*Comes running out with a jar of red paint which he puts on the top of the cask while he stoops down and examines the stain on the floor again.*) Ah—this isn't blood. It's paint. (*Standing up again.*) Somebody's been painting here.

LISA. Who do you suppose it was?

SALVATORE. I don't know.

LISA. And what's he been painting? It must have been a picture, but I don't see any. Do you?

SALVATORE. It must be hidden. Whoever's been doing the painting hid his paints. He hid what he painted, too.

LISA. There isn't any place to hide it in this room.

SALVATORE. There may be a secret panel or something.

LISA. A secret panel in a plastered wall? How funny you are, Salvatore.

SALVATORE. Let's look and see, anyway. (*Both feel about*

quickly. SALVATORE *finally gets on bench, feels the cover.*)
Lisa!

LISA. It's loose. (*Both pull it back enough to see, but the audience can't.*) How beautiful! This *is* a picture! See the Baby and the flowers! I wonder who could have painted it?

SALVATORE. Nobody that lives in Cadore. I know that. Even I couldn't do anything like this. It's some great artist! Maybe it's the great master Bellini, making it to give to Cadore!

LISA. And we're the first to find it out! Wait! There's a name here. Is it Bellini?

SALVATORE. It's all mixed up in the flowers. Why didn't he put it so it could be seen easily, the way I have mine?

LISA. Look—there's a T-i-

SALVATORE. Z-i-a-

LISA. No. That's T-i-z-i-a-n-o—Tiziano! Is that Bellini's first name?

SALVATORE. I don't know, but it must be if he's put it here. Here's the other name. V-e-c- That's not the way you spell Bellini. What is it? What is it, Lisa?

LISA. E-l-l-i. What is that? Vecelli?

SALVATORE. Tiziano Vecelli? Tiziano—oh, no! No!

LISA. It's his name. He couldn't make a picture like this.

SALVATORE. Oh, couldn't he? He's done it, hasn't he? But it won't do him any good. He won't win the prize. He won't! He won't! He won't! (*Dashes away from the painting like a wild thing. Looks all about for something with which to ruin the painting.*) I'll stop that! (*Laughter outside.*)

LISA. What are you going to do? (*Laughter is louder. Someone calls "Lisa! Salvatore!"* CARLOTTA *and* PEPITA *try door, then climb in the window.*)

PEPITA. Here you are!

CARLOTTA. We knew you'd be here ahead.

PEPITA. Everybody is calling for you! They're ready to set out to see the places where the pictures were painted. Very soon you will hear them passing.

SALVATORE. You go along. Lisa's not going.

PEPITA. Why, she was chosen by the whole town to lead the dance before the procession.

CARLOTTA. We can't do our part without her.

SALVATORE. Do something else, then.

CARLOTTA. Oh, Lisa, please, I was never chosen for a dance before.

PEPITA. You'll be ashamed, Salvatore, if your picture wins and your sister's not in the dance that brings the master here.

SALVATORE. I don't care whether she's in it or not! She's forgotten the steps anyway, haven't you, Lisa? (*Distant Italian dance music.*)

LISA. Well—yes, I'd spoil it anyway.

PEPITA. You have not forgotten the steps. You don't want to dance with us, that's it. You think you're too good for us.

CARLOTTA. We'll show you. You'll remember as soon as we begin.

PEPITA. Yes, come on. Here's your garland. (*They dance. SALVATORE furiously, but stealthily, throws all the paint out of the window except the red. LISA sees and tries to hide what he is doing. SALVATORE finishes. The music swells.*)

SALVATORE. Lisa! Don't you hear! They're coming!

PEPITA (*pulling at LISA*). Come on.

SALVATORE (*pulling on her other hand*). I want you. (*Music fades.*)

CARLOTTA. They're not coming here after all. (*Looks out.*)

PEPITA. They're going to Tonio's first.

CARLOTTA. They'll come here last because it's farthest from the town hall.

PEPITA. If you want Lisa to do something, hurry then. We'll wait.

SALVATORE. We don't want you around. Go on!

LISA. I'll come in a minute.

PEPITA. I'd like to know what's the matter with you.

SALVATORE. Nothing!

PEPITA. Why are you so anxious to get rid of us?

CARLOTTA. You know something!

PEPITA. You're hiding something you don't want us to find out. Well, we will find out. (*Sits down.*) Sit down, Carlotta. We aren't going to go until he tells.

SALVATORE. Miss the dance, if you like. I won't tell if you sit all day.

CARLOTTA. They're starting out again. Please come, Lisa. We're missing it now. I don't care about his old secret. I want to go to the dance.

PEPITA. Will you come right away?

LISA. Yes, I'll catch up with you. Go. Hurry.

SALVATORE. The sooner you go the quicker she'll come.

CARLOTTA (*climbing through window*). Come on, Pepita.

PEPITA (*climbing through window*). All right for you, Salvatore. I'll find out sometime. (*They run off.*)

LISA. Why wouldn't you let me go?

SALVATORE. Hold up the cover, quick!

LISA. What are you going to do?

SALVATORE. I'm going to fix Tiziano Vecelli! He'll never show his picture. (LISA *drops the cover and snatches at the paint he holds.*) Let go.

LISA. Oh, Salvatore, don't! Are you mad?

SALVATORE (*puts his hand in the paint and smears it on her dress*). Get out of my way or I'll put it all over you.

LISA. Oh, my new dress! Oh, Salvatore! (*She rushes and throws paint out. He runs for jar of dirty water, lifts cover and splashes it on. Down on his knees he begins to smear it over the painting, leaving a clear print of his hand.* TIZIANO *and* CATARINA, *singing off.* LISA, *frantic, runs to* SALVATORE.) Salvatore! You can't do that to the Madonna! It's a sin! It's a sin!

SALVATORE (*after hesitation*). Well—that's enough to stop his showing it, anyway. (*They drop the cover, carry the jars into the other room, and suddenly become conscious of the approaching voices. They start for the window.*)

LISA. Oh—they'll see us!

SALVATORE. Hush! We can go out this way. Hurry, run! (*They exit through the little door, pushing it almost shut as they leave.* CATARINA's *head appears at the window over the huge armful of flowers that she heaps on the window sill.* TIZIANO *unlocks and comes through the door. They finish the song they are singing as he enters.* TIZIANO *begins to arrange his huge bouquet in the cask near the picture.*)

TIZIANO. Catarina!

CATARINA. What, Tiziano?

TIZIANO. Do you remember the day we planned to make the picture?

CATARINA. Yes, indeed, I do. You were so sad about losing your paints, and then you were so happy when you found the flower paints. Why?

TIZIANO. And after I told you what I was going to paint you sang the Madonna song. Remember?

CATARINA. Mm.

TIZIANO. Sing it again now, for Her, and I'll take one more

look to see how She likes it, and then you must go for the
master. Will you?

CATARINA. Yes, I'll sing it. (*She begins the song, still holding
the flowers in front of her in the window. In the meantime*
TIZIANO *goes to look at the picture and discovers the stain.
He backs away from the picture with both hands over his
mouth.*)

TIZIANO. Catarina! Catarina!

CATARINA. What is it? Oh, what is it, Tiziano?

TIZIANO. My picture! My beautiful picture! (CATARINA *drops
the flowers and comes running in.* TIZIANO *holds up the end
of the cover. She stands speechless with horror.* TIZIANO
drops the cover.)

CURTAIN

ACT THREE

SCENE: *Same as Act Two. Five minutes later.*

As the curtain rises TIZIANO *is hiding his face against the
cover of the painting. He is trying not to cry.*

CATARINA. Who could have done such a wicked thing?

TIZIANO. I don't know.

CATARINA. You didn't tell anyone about your picture, did
you?

TIZIANO. No, of course not.

CATARINA. Then somebody must have been watching you.

TIZIANO. I suppose so.

CATARINA. But who? Who would be likely to come this way?
What would anyone be doing in this old house?

TIZIANO. I don't know, but it doesn't matter. I can't show my

picture now. The great master will never know how I love
to paint. I'll never go to Venice.

CATARINA. Oh—Tiziano—and your picture is so beautiful!

TIZIANO. I know it.

CATARINA. Can't you show it anyway?

TIZIANO (astounded). No!

CATARINA. But why not? Please let me go for the master.

TIZIANO. No, Catarina—no. I don't even want to see it myself.

CATARINA. Oh, Tiziano, after all this work! Can't you do
something about it? Can't you paint the flowers over
again? You could paint it while I go for the master.

TIZIANO (taking heart, lifts the cover to look). Yes, I could.
See, it could be covered with fresh paint and hardly
noticed. The red here is smeared. I'll put blue over it—
like violet shadow.

CATARINA. And the yellow is smeared, too.

TIZIANO. Blue over that will make it look like dark green
leaves. Quick, Rina, get me the paint.

CATARINA. The blue?

TIZIANO. And the red, too.

CATARINA. Then give me the key.

TIZIANO (runs to the hiding place). It's gone!

CATARINA. Look! It's in the door! (Tries handle.) It's open.

TIZIANO (pushing her aside, rushes in). Oh—

CATARINA. What's wrong?

TIZIANO (entering slowly). The paints! They're all gone.
(Locks door, absently puts key in pocket.) I can't do the
flowers over again.

CATARINA. Who could have done it? I think we ought to tell
Father Anton about this. He'd find out who it was.

TIZIANO. We're not going to tell anybody. I don't want to
know who did it.

CATARINA. I do!

TIZIANO. I couldn't bear to know.

CATARINA. I could. I'd like to find out who he is—and do something about it. That's what I'd like. You would, too. You know you would.

TIZIANO. No! No! I'd run if I saw him coming.

CATARINA. Why?

TIZIANO. I don't know. I couldn't bear to look at him. It's too horrible a thing for anyone to do. It doesn't seem so real as long as I don't know him.

CATARINA. You wouldn't want him to see how much you cared.

TIZIÁNO. Oh—it doesn't matter who sees that. I do care—I do.

CATARINA. I'm sorry, Tiziano. Then you're not going to do anything about it at all?

TIZIANO. No.

CATARINA. Then you're a silly, foolish boy, even if you are my own brother. Besides, I think it's wrong, what you're doing. Somebody did a bad thing and should be punished.

TIZIANO. What's the use of punishing him?

CATARINA. If he were punished, he wouldn't do bad things like that again.

TIZIANO. Yes, he would. He's that kind. He'd just be more careful not to be caught next time.

CATARINA. It would make me glad to see him sorry for what he's done.

TIZIANO. What good would that do? It wouldn't make my picture right.

CATARINA. Do you suppose it was a man or a boy who did it?

TIZIANO. I don't know.

CATARINA. May I look at the picture again?

TIZIANO. If you want to.

CATARINA (*looks and discovers the print of a hand on the painting, puts her own beside it*). It wasn't a man. It was somebody our size. The print of his hand is right here. It wasn't Tonio. He wouldn't do such a thing. Tiziano—could it be Salvatore?

TIZIANO. He'd do it. It's like him.

CATARINA. I'm going for Father Anton.

TIZIANO. No, don't. You mustn't.

CATARINA. Why not?

TIZIANO. We wouldn't dare tell on Salvatore. The Signor Zampanti would do terrible things to Father.

CATARINA. Oh—yes, he would. You painted on his doublet, too.

TIZIANO. Come along.

CATARINA. What are you going to do?

TIZIANO. What is there to do? I don't want to stay here.

CATARINA. Where are you going?

TIZIANO. Anywhere! Anywhere that isn't here! (*Music, off, not too loud. Shouts—"Bravo!", "Bellini!", etc.*)

CATARINA. Do you care if I stay here?

TIZIANO. What for?

CATARINA. Well, I've heard that sometimes when a person's done something bad, he comes back to the place. If I stayed, I might find out something.

TIZIANO. What's the use of finding out? Come with me. (*Music and shouts nearer.*)

CATARINA. Hear them! Everyone is happy. They're shouting for Bellini.

TIZIANO (*listens in despair, then lifts his face, slowly showing a change in his feelings*). The great Bellini! I can see him, at least. I can look into his face. I can hear his voice. I'm going to find him, Catarina. I'm going to cheer for him, too. He'll never see my picture, but there's something I'm going to give him. Stay if you like. But don't forget your promise to the Madonna. (*Exits.* CATARINA *begins to look about for clues. She looks out of the window and sees* ZAMPANTI *and* SALVATORE *coming and decides to hide. She tries to get in the storeroom. It is locked so she finally climbs into the cask—just in time.* SALVATORE *and his father enter.*)

ZAMPANTI. Well now, son, what is all the hurry about? Say what it is you have to surprise me with, unless you want the others to share it. They'll be here any minute.

SALVATORE. Well, first look at this wall. Do you notice anything strange about it?

ZAMPANTI. Strange? (*Going toward it.*) It's covered.

SALVATORE. Look behind the cover. (*Lifts the cover, opposite the smear. While they are doing this* CATARINA *peeks out.*) Now!

ZAMPANTI. A painting! What beauty! Salvatore, my son, you are really a genius. You're clever, too. You make a small sketch that is better than all the rest put together, but you save *this* for the big surprise. Such talent! I can hardly believe it.

SALVATORE. But, Father, you don't understand.

ZAMPANTI. No—I don't. I'm not an artist. I'm a ruler of men. But this I do understand. You shall go to Venice and the world will be at your feet in no time. Princes will fight to have you in their palaces. Now our position is safe. The name of Zampanti will go down in history. I'm proud of you, my boy. When you leave for Venice—

SALVATORE. But, Father, listen to me—

ZAMPANTI. This town shall have the grandest festival ever known in Italy.

SALVATORE. It's all wrong, what you're saying.

ZAMPANTI. Not a bit of it! It shall be just as I say.

SALVATORE. It isn't my painting.

ZAMPANTI. What? Then who—?

SALVATORE. It's Tiziano Vecelli's.

ZAMPANTI. Tiziano Vecelli! The boy who painted on the shoe?

SALVATORE. It's true. But don't look like that, Father. See what I did to it! See what I did to it!

ZAMPANTI. You did that? Oh— Oh— (*They both laugh.*)

SALVATORE. Tiziano didn't enter the contest at all. I knew he wouldn't. So it's all right, isn't it?

ZAMPANTI. Yes—if he doesn't appear while Bellini and the others are here.

SALVATORE. He won't! He'd never want to show this.

ZAMPANTI. I hope you're right. If this painting is discovered everything will be over between us and the Prince.

SALVATORE. Oh, no, Father.

ZAMPANTI. I urged the Prince to have Bellini come. I told him about you. I've praised your talent everywhere, and now a cobbler's apprentice has surpassed you. Why didn't you stop him?

SALVATORE. I didn't know he was doing it.

ZAMPANTI. You should have had wit enough to watch him.

SALVATORE. I thought you'd be glad when you saw how I stopped him from showing his picture.

ZAMPANTI. Well—perhaps you did the best you could. We can only hope the picture isn't discovered until after you've been proclaimed the winner. That's all. If it should be, there's nothing I can do about it while Bellini's here. He'd tell the Prince. But I'll settle the Vecellis once and for all after he's gone. (*Music and singing heard approach-*

ing.) They're coming. Keep people with their backs to the wall so the picture won't be discovered. (*Music and dancing entrance.* PEPITA, LISA, CARLOTTA *throwing flowers and dancing before* BELLINI *and* FATHER ANTON. LUCIA VECELLI *and* MARIA ZAMPANTI *follow.*) Welcome, welcome, Signor Bellini. (*He tries to move him C with his back to the picture.* BELLINI, *however, draws away and stands looking about.*)

BELLINI. Thank you, Signor; you are very gracious.

ZAMPANTI. My son is impatient to show you the scene of his painting.

SALVATORE. Yes, Signor Bellini. Shall I show you where to stand?

BELLINI. No, no. Not yet. (*He looks about, delighted.*) Let me see if I can find out from the title. What do you call it?

SALVATORE. A Deserted House.

BELLINI. I shouldn't call it that, no matter where I stood. There's another spirit here. A deserted house is lonely and sad. There's joy here.

FATHER A. Do you feel it, too?

BELLINI. It's as if the place were trying to tell us something happy.

PEPITA. What does he mean?

CARLOTTA. I know.

BELLINI. You have made a delightful choice. If you have the spirit of this place in your painting, my visit here has not been in vain. What lovely flowers! How they fit into the spirit of it.

FATHER A. Yes, they are just right. Where did you get them, Salvatore?

SALVATORE. I—out there—

FATHER A. How fresh they are! I didn't know there were any
of these so near.

CARLOTTA. Tell us where they grow, Salvatore, and we'll
gather some for the master now.

SALVATORE. We—we picked all there were—Lisa and I.

FATHER A. Where do they grow? I thought I knew the homes
of all the flowers near Cadore. These are very rare.

SALVATORE. Yes, Father. I know they are—

ZAMPANTI. Show the master your picture, son.

BELLINI. First let us see whether the young artist made a good
choice of what to paint. It's a pity a picture can take in
only one little part of this room.

ZAMPANTI. I think you should stand here.

BELLINI. Let me follow my own ideas, if you please. I have—
whims—of my own about what makes a good painting.
(*Moves to look DL.*) There's a picture from here—an interesting difference in the tone of the two walls. (*Toward
storeroom door.*) There is more variety from here. But
none of the charm of the place. None of the spirit I felt
as I came in. (*Toward window.*) Ah! Here is a picture
worth any artist. The mountains! With the lake at the
foot, framed by the window. The seat below waiting for
someone to look out and wonder at their beauty. Sit here,
child. Let's finish our picture. (CARLOTTA *obeys.*) I think
I shall come and paint this myself some day, if Salvatore
chose some other scene. The happy child, the lovely flowers, and in the background the mountains and lake of
Cadore. Now let's find another. (*He turns square back,
facing wall with picture.*)

ZAMPANTI (*hurriedly, in spite of his care*). There's surely
nothing there. (BELLINI *lifts a hand to check him.* FATHER
ANTON *moves to study his face more closely.*)

BELLINI. Not from here. That's true. But (*toward audience*) from here, with the sun coming through that high window, as it will bye and bye—and falling across Father Anton, there— (*Moves into position for* SALVATORE's *picture.*) Yes, here, too, is a picture. The door—the cask—the bit of red on the floor. What a wonderful red it is! How perfectly placed for a picture painted from where I stand. Well, the mountains through the window would be the best choice. The high window at the time the sun pours through it, and this with the bit of red on the floor, are next. One would be as good as another. Did you choose any of them, Salvatore? (*He holds out hand for picture.*)

SALVATORE. I painted my picture from just where you are standing. (*He gives it to him.*)

BELLINI. That's a very good sense of composition. Did you paint the red on the floor yourself?

SALVATORE. No.

BELLINI. Why, it isn't in your picture at all!

SALVATORE. It—it wasn't there when I painted this.

BELLINI. That's a pity. Well, well—this is all very accurate. Everything is here—except the spirit I caught as I came in. And the cask isn't in quite the right relation to the door.

SALVATORE. Why, sir, we placed it just right—or—that is—

BELLINI. It should be a little more to this side. Move it and you will see. (SALVATORE *starts to move it. It is too heavy.* ZAMPANTI *lends a hand.*)

GREGORIO. Tip it, Signor. (ZAMPANTI *starts to.* CATARINA *cries. The cover moves. They hastily set the cask upright again. All start back.*)

ZAMPANTI. There is someone hiding there!

SALVATORE. He was there—all the time.

LISA. Do you suppose—

SALVATORE. Sh-h—

MARIA. There's always someone spying on my husband. Waiting to do him harm.

ZAMPANTI. I am armed! Leave me alone with him.

FATHER A. We'll have no violence, please. Put up your sword.

ZAMPANTI. How do we know there aren't others waiting for a signal from him?

FATHER A. No one will hurt me or any I protect.

ZAMPANTI. I protect myself. You, in there. If you don't come out I'll run you through. Now, come on—and come hands first. (CATARINA's *hands appear, clutching a bunch of flowers.*)

MARIA. It's a child!

GREGORIO. Catarina! What are you doing here?

LUCIA. Catarina!

SALVATORE. It's his sister!

LISA. She was listening.

ZAMPANTI. What do you mean by such impudence? You're a Vecelli, aren't you? (LISA *and* SALVATORE *start to slip out.* FATHER ANTON *cuts across them all.*)

FATHER A. Wait a minute! Catarina, what were you doing in the cask? (*He helps her out.*)

CATARINA. I wanted to get out, Father, but there wasn't any chance.

FATHER A. That doesn't explain why you were in there.

CATARINA. I—

ZAMPANTI. She doesn't need to explain. She can hold her tongue and go home. I allow no child to be impudent to me.

FATHER A. She does need to explain, Signor Zampanti, because I asked her to. Catarina, you need not be afraid. Why were you in there?

CATARINA. I wanted to find out something.

ZAMPANTI. Signor Bellini is here to judge my son's picture.

FATHER A. By your leave, Signor. I think this is something which must be settled now.

BELLINI. I am at your service, Father Anton.

FATHER A. Catarina, what did you want to find out?

CATARINA. I—I can't tell.

FATHER A. Yes, you can, child. You need fear no one. No one at all. Now tell me bravely. What did you wish to find out?

CATARINA. I can't, you see, Father, because I made a promise on the cross. I can't break that, can I?

FATHER A. No, that promise you must keep. (*Pointing a finger suddenly at* SALVATORE.) Salvatore, why did you and Lisa want to go just now?

CATARINA (*following his pointing hand*). Oh-h—it was you! (*Darting to snatch* SALVATORE's *hand.*) And your hand! I knew it was you!

SALVATORE. Keep away from me.

CATARINA. I knew it! There's nobody else in Cadore bad and wicked enough to do such a thing!

SALVATORE. Leave me alone!

ZAMPANTI. Gregorio, take this child away from here! I've had enough impertinence from you Vecellis. Your taxes are not paid. Your children break into Signor Bellini's judging! Let there be no more, or I promise you shall suffer for it.

BELLINI. I am interested in what the child says, Signor. Pray do not stop her on my account.

MARIA. She shall not go on saying evil things of my children. They have done no wrong.

LUCIA. Are you sure? Your children are afraid of her. Look and see.

MARIA. Your child has made some promise on the cross. Why? It looks to me as if she were the one who had done something wrong. She would not do that for nothing.

LUCIA. No, it was yours!

MARIA. It was yours—

FATHER A. Signora! Signora! Lucia, you are right in one thing. Salvatore and Lisa are afraid. Maria is also right. Catarina would not make a promise on the cross for nothing. What is the wicked thing they have done, Catarina?

CATARINA. I can't tell.

FATHER A. Why are your children afraid, Maria?

MARIA. Something wicked the Vecelli child has done.

FATHER A. Do you know, Signor?

ZAMPANTI. Of course not! This is some child's affair! It's time we got back to the pictures!

FATHER A. Catarina, have you done anything to Salvatore and Lisa to make them afraid of you?

CATARINA. No!

FATHER A. Then are you trying to shield them?

CATARINA. No!

FATHER A. (to LISA and SALVATORE). Do you know why Catarina was hiding?

LISA, SALVATORE. No!

FATHER A. Are you sure you don't, children?

MARIA. Do you doubt my children's word?

FATHER A. I do.

MARIA. Father Anton, this is a presumption on your part. You are speaking of the children of the Signor Zampanti.

FATHER A. We are all the children of the Blessed Lord, Signora. Guilt is guilt to me wherever I see it.

ZAMPANTI. That is quite enough, Father Anton. Shall we proceed, Signor Bellini?

BELLINI. Not quite yet. There is a bit of color here that interests me. This red on the floor—on your dress (*indicating* LISA)—on your hand (*indicating* SALVATORE). How did it come there? It looks like paint. Is it?

CATARINA. Yes.

FATHER A. How did it get there? Do you know, Catarina?

CATARINA. Yes, but I cannot tell.

FATHER A. Is there any of it on Salvatore's painting?

BELLINI. No—why didn't you use it, Salvatore? It's more beautiful than *this* red. (SALVATORE *is silent.*) It's wonderful! Who makes it here? Where can I get some to take back to Venice?

FATHER A. It's not made here. It can't be bought in Cadore.

BELLINI. It's fresh paint. I know by the look of it. It's been made right here.

ZAMPANTI. Nonsense. Everyone is waiting for you, Signor Bellini.

BELLINI. Such color as this isn't seen every day. They'll have to wait until I find out where it came from.

FATHER A. And who has used it. I think Catarina knows—I think Salvatore knows, too.

BELLINI. I think this signorina knows how this red came on her dress and on her brother's hand. (*Indicating* LISA, *who bursts out crying.*)

ZAMPANTI. This is enough! You are a very great man, Signor Bellini, but you have no right to drive my children to tears.

BELLINI. The Prince has sent me to Cadore to look for a youth to train in painting for his service. I am about to award the position to your son. I must understand what all this means before I do. Salvatore, if you wish to go to

Venice you must tell how you got that paint on your hand.

SALVATORE. I found it in a jar in there. I threw it out—there. That's how it got on my hand.

BELLINI. You expect to be an artist, and yet you throw out such color as this?

SALVATORE. I didn't think of that.

FATHER A. What did you think of—why did you throw it out? Answer, Salvatore.

SALVATORE. I don't know.

FATHER A. How did it come to be there?

SALVATORE. It was just in jars.

BELLINI. Were there any other colors?

SALVATORE. Yes, sir.

BELLINI. What?

SALVATORE. Blue—yellow—I don't remember.

BELLINI. Where are they?

SALVATORE. I threw them all out.

BELLINI. You did that? And they weren't yours?

FATHER A. Who brought them here? Did you?

SALVATORE. No—I found them, when I came.

FATHER A. In this room?

SALVATORE. No, in there.

FATHER A. Then the door wasn't locked when you came?

SALVATORE. Yes, it was.

FATHER A. Then how did you get in?

SALVATORE. There was a key.

FATHER A. You had a key?

SALVATORE. No—I found it. It was hidden.

ZAMPANTI. I can't see what interest you can have in such details. Signor Bellini cannot find out what he wants to know about this paint from my children.

MARIA. You see that my Salvatore knows nothing about it.

FATHER A. Then why did he throw the paint out?

MARIA. He was making the room bright for your coming, Signor. You can't blame him for that.

BELLINI. I'd blame the Prince himself if he were to throw out color like that red.

LUCIA. It looks like the stains on my floor from the poppies.

BELLINI. Let me see. (*Takes flowers and crosses with them to* LISA.) Could it have been made from flowers? Where did these flowers come from?

FATHER A. (*very severely*). Salvatore, did you tell the truth when you said you got these flowers—out there? Answer!

SALVATORE. Well—no.

FATHER A. Salvatore, did you bring them in?

SALVATORE. No.

FATHER A. Lisa?

LISA. No!

FATHER A. Catarina?

CATARINA. No—well—not those. (*Looks at flowers in her hand.*)

FATHER A. These then? (*Points to color on the floor.*) Did you help someone make this color?

CATARINA. Don't, please, ask me any more.

FATHER A. That's what she promised not to tell! But if the color was here for Salvatore to throw out, it must have been used here. Where? The canvas must be in there. (*Pointing to storeroom.*)

BELLINI. This looks like fresco paint. It would be on a wall, not on a canvas. (*Looks around and suddenly points to the covered wall.* FATHER ANTON *draws the cover off. In awe.*) Who did this? (*In horror.*) What's happened here?

FATHER A. Salvatore, put your hand on this. (*Indicates hand print.*)

SALVATORE. No. (FATHER ANTON *takes his hand.*) I won't. (FATHER ANTON *makes him.*)

ZAMPANTI. Let the boy alone.

BELLINI. Your son has smeared this painting, Signor Zampanti. His hand fits exactly.

ZAMPANTI, MARIA. Signor—!! You are bold. (SALVATORE *slumps to his knees.*)

FATHER A. (*softly*). Stand up, Salvatore. (SALVATORE *rises.*)

BELLINI (*hands* SALVATORE *his canvas*). Here is your painting, young sir. This fresco wins the contest.

ZAMPANTI. That is impossible, Signor. The boy who painted that hasn't a ducat! He couldn't pay to live in Venice for a day!

BELLINI. How do you know that?

SALVATORE. It's only Tiziano Vecelli.

ZAMPANTI. It's signed.

BELLINI. So it is. Your eyes are good, Signor Zampanti.

LUCIA. Tiziano—?

FATHER A. Yes.

LUCIA. Our Tiziano?

FATHER A. Yes.

GREGORIO. He could do a thing like that?

CATARINA. Please don't be angry with him, Father. He had to do it.

GREGORIO. I didn't know it was such a thing he wished to do.

LUCIA. No one could look at that and feel angry.

GREGORIO. That I should have such a son!

LUCIA. Oh, Signor Zampanti, have mercy about the taxes. Let Gregorio keep part of his earnings to send our boy to Venice to study—

ZAMPANTI. You are behind on your payment already.

LUCIA. But look! It seems he is not like other boys—

ZAMPANTI. I have said no.

LUCIA. Then take this old house in payment. It is dear to us. Fortune has not always been against us. It has belonged to a Vecelli from early times. But for this we will part with it—

GREGORIO. Yes, Signor—for this.

ZAMPANTI. I will take it, yes. It will wipe out part of your debt. But not the whole of it. Let Tiziano bring me his wages regularly for the rest.

LUCIA. But Venice—

ZAMPANTI. He will never go to Venice.

BELLINI. You are mistaken. The boy who did this shall have every chance Venice can give him.

ZAMPANTI. Do you think to interfere with the money that is mine, and which means my favor with the Prince?

BELLINI. There are things worth more than gold, Signor, and more than the favor of princes. (*During this last,* TIZIANO *enters and stands looking at* BELLINI. *He carries the shoe on which the Madonna is painted. He goes to* BELLINI *and drops on his knees.*)

TIZIANO (*breathless*). Signor Bellini—

BELLINI. Who is this?

TIZIANO. You are the great Bellini!

BELLINI. I am Bellini. How did you know that?

TIZIANO. I have thought of you. You were just like this. I have brought you a little gift. Will you take it? It is a small thing. But I am poor. I would give you the whole world if I could. (*Offers him the shoe.*)

BELLINI. On the sole of a shoe—

TIZIANO. I am a cobbler's apprentice.

BELLINI (*turns to compare it with the painting*). So you are Tiziano Vecelli?

TIZIANO. Yes, Signor.

BELLINI. Signor Zampanti, how much is it Gregorio owes you? Everything. The full sum.

ZAMPANTI. It is fifty ducats. It grows because he falls behind on his payments.

BELLINI. Fifty ducats?

ZAMPANTI. Yes.

BELLINI. That is exact?

ZAMPANTI. It is exact.

BELLINI. Here is the sum. (*Takes a few coins out of purse and gives them to* ZAMPANTI.)

FATHER A. We are witnesses that your debt is paid.

BELLINI. Take it—and go out of my sight. (*To* SALVATORE.) You, too.

ZAMPANTI (*at exit*). You will hear of this day's work.

BELLINI. So shall you, Signor, and men who live long after us. Tiziano Vecelli no longer belongs to us or to any man, but to the whole world. (*He hands purse to* GREGORIO.) I give it to you to make up for your son's wages while he is in Venice with me. Will you go to Venice with me, Tiziano Vecelli, to learn to be a great painter?

CURTAIN

PRODUCTION NOTES

SETTING   The action can be played against a cyclorama or drapes with set pieces or screens, or in a basic box set, with interchangeable plugs.

STAGE PROPERTIES

ACT ONE

> Two doors
> Large window
> Fireplace
> Drop-leaf table
> Bench
> Chair
> Crucifix

ACTS TWO AND THREE

> Two doors (same as Act One)
> Large window (same as Act One)
> Painting on wall, covered by hanging which matches wall
> Bench, under window
> Wine cask or barrel, with cover, large enough to hide
> > CATARINA
> Brazier
> Smaller cask, in which fresh flowers are arranged
> Bench or plank on two kegs, under painting (optional, depending on height of painting)
> Platform (optional)

HAND PROPERTIES

ACT ONE

Two pairs of shoes	TIZIANO
Small package of paints	"
Pieces of colored glass	"
Piece of charcoal, paint brush, paints	"

Wrapping paper	TIZIANO
Thread and needle	"
Shawl	"
Doll	"
Coins	" and VECELLI
Water bucket	LUCIA
Doublet	ZAMPANTI
Scroll	"
Garland of flowers	LISA
Wreath	CARLOTTA
Bouquets	CATARINA and PEPITA
Cloth	"

ACT TWO

Jars of paint	TIZIANO
Brushes	"
Key	"
Flowers	CATARINA
Jar of glue (water can be used)	"
Flowers	" and TIZIANO
Picture	SALVATORE
Garland of flowers	PEPITA

ACT THREE

Shoe, on which Madonna is painted	TIZIANO
Purse filled with coins	BELLINI

COSTUMES   In a historical play, such as this, it is important that the producer pay careful attention to costume which must be accurate for the period. This does not necessarily mean that all details and decoration be duplicated, but rather that the silhouette and fashions conform to the period. The amount of detail will depend on the degree of realism with which the production is treated. There is a wealth of written material on costumes of this period and, of course, the paintings and drawings by artists of the time, such as Bellini, provide an excellent source for both costume and scene design.

The dress of BELLINI and the members of the ZAMPANTI FAMILY should be distinguished, by richness of materials and detail, from that of the rest of the characters.

MUSIC

ACTS ONE AND TWO

CATARINA'S song—an appropriate lullaby

ACT TWO

CATARINA'S and TIZIANA'S song—early folk song

ACTS TWO AND THREE

BELLINI'S welcome—peasant street dance music

SOUND

ACT ONE

Church bells for the angelus

The Secret of
the Worn-out Shoes

A FAIRY TALE FOR DANCE DRAMA

BY MARGARET ELLEN CLIFFORD

EDITORS' NOTE

The Secret of the Worn-out Shoes takes its inspiration from the old folk tale, *The Twelve Dancing Princesses* which, as so many medieval tales do, symbolizes the struggle between life and death, light and darkness. The play preserves the original devices of the enchanted woods, lake and castle, the talisman of the broken branch, and the golden cup, and adds others consistent with this form of myth. It has the flavor of an eighteenth-century version of the story because of the use it makes of class distinctions; but its most interesting contribution is the modern interpretation of the theme: that the power of superstition and social difficulties, alike, stem from the fear in one's own heart.

This may very well provide the introduction of early teen-agers to stylized acting. The playwright has, in many instances, included precise and detailed directions used in the play's first production, all of which may be changed at the director's discretion. However, these directions tell, better than any description, the manner of playing envisioned by the author. Such an assignment is not impossible for young players since the characterizations are individualized and the language is very simple and without artificiality.

This play is an addition to lyric theatre which requires players both to move and to speak (actors who dance and dancers who speak). The theme of the play is externalized in terms of dance, the conflict being revealed in the contrast between conventional, formalized dance and free interpretive dance. It offers a fine opportunity for collaboration between dance and drama directors. It also affords the chance to use in dramatic production any experience gained from choral speaking.

The parts of Michael and Lina may have to be taken by older young people with more dance training than the rest of the cast. None of the dances need be long or have elaborate choreography. If necessary, some may be cut—specifically, the first gypsy dance and the dressing table ballet. However, a sharp contrast between the traditional peasant dance, the formal patterns of Lina's solo and the pavane, as opposed to Michael's free dance, must be clearly shown.

If a larger cast is desired, villagers can be brought in with the gypsies' entrance in Act One. If doubling is necessary, the Herald and gypsies can play the parts of the Princes and the Lady of the Stars and two of the water-carriers the parts of the Laurels. The play may readily be done by an all-female cast.

The Secret of the Worn-out Shoes allows to an unusual extent for the integration of imaginative design, lighting, music, dance and acting in an absorbingly dramatic and unified story.

THE SECRET OF
THE WORN-OUT SHOES
A Fairy Tale for Dance Drama

CHARACTERS

MICHAEL, a shepherd boy

LADY OF THE STARS

OLD GYPSY WOMAN

THE KING

THE HERALD

CELESTINA, the eldest ⎫
MARIETTA
FLORENTINA
LIZABETTA
ERNESTINA   ⎬ Princesses, ages 15 to 23
HENRIETTA
PAULINA
LORETTA
LINA, the youngest ⎭

KATRINKA ⎫
HEDJE
HEIDI
MARITJE
GRETCHEN ⎬ Nine Little Girls
MARTA
FREDA
SARA
LISA ⎭

THE CHERRY LAUREL

THE ROSE LAUREL

EIGHT PRINCES

A BAND OF GYPSY DANCERS

Villagers may be added if desired

Some doubling may be done if necessary

PLACE: *A kingdom in middle Europe*

TIME: *The eighteenth century*

ACT ONE: *The village square*

Early morning of May Day

ACT TWO: *The princesses' dressing room*

Morning of a day several weeks later

ACT THREE, Scene One: *The same*

The next night

Scene Two: *The enchanted castle*

A moment later

NOTE ON THE SETTINGS *

The entire play can be done in drapes with set pieces, or with completely conceived and executed sets. If the latter is undertaken care must be exercised to leave sufficient free stage space for the dancing.

In Act One, the village square, the only essential element is a weathered medieval fountain or well around which is a stone

---

* Full production notes will be found at the end of the play.

bench. If houses are added, they should be of the peasant architecture of a middle European country of the designer's choice.
Bright colors, gaily carved shutters, some wall paintings, will em-
phasize the folk atmosphere in contrast to the later settings.
Several entrances between the houses are essential.

The dressing room of Act Two and Act Three, Scene One,
should reflect the delicacy and conventional aristocratic elegance
of eighteenth-century baroque décor. Where curtains are used
for a background, this effect can be achieved in the silhouette
and details of the two door units and with fairly elaborate dressing tables, with their feminine drapery. If some variation of a
box set is used the laurel trees must be in front of jogs or entrances, or placed in some other such way so that the spirits of
the trees can emerge from behind them easily. The dressing room
scenes do not call for a deep set. If the stage is large enough, the
dressing room can be set up in front of the enchanted castle scene.

The enchanted castle of Act Three, Scene Two, must seem to
change from a mysterious ballroom to a spot in the actual palace
garden. By assuming that the locale is an open summer pavilion,
the set can be simply composed of columns, with capitals joined
by garlands or cloth swags, and some formal greenery. The
other-world, dreamlike atmosphere disappears with the light
change required when the goblet is broken, the strong light bringing out actual colors and shapes of objects.

ACT ONE

SCENE: *The square of a middle European village. The village
well, C,* has a broad stone seat around it. It is early morning
of May Day.*

*The stage is empty at the rise of the curtain, but almost
immediately we hear the cry of the water-carriers and* NINE

---

* The following abbreviations are used throughout: C—center
stage; R—right stage; L—left stage; U—upstage; D—downstage.

LITTLE GIRLS, carrying jars on their heads, enter and circle the fountain.

GIRLS (chanting).

> Water! Water! Clear fresh water!
> Water for the village! Water!
> Water to wash with,
> Water to cook with,
> Clear fresh water! Water! Water!

(When the leader has come around to the front of the fountain, she steps up on the stone seat and fills her jar, then fills each of the others as the GIRLS file past her, humming the chant as they go. They are grave and serious while attending to business, but as soon as the last jar is filled, the 2nd one in line kicks the girl in front of her lightly, the 4th pinches the 3rd, and so forth down the line. The 1st, 3rd, etc., squeal, the line breaks. Half set down their jars L of the fountain, half to R. They chase each other around, giggling and squealing, until several are tired and flop down, with the leader still C at the well bench.)

KATRINKA (the leader, who has not joined in the nonsense). There! At least the jars are all filled, even if you do have to romp and be silly.

HEDJE. Oh, Katrinka, how can you be so serious? Don't you remember what day it is today?

HEIDI. I do! (Others join her.) It's May Day!

MARITJE. It's the day of the May Day festival.

GRETCHEN. This morning there were May baskets at everybody's door.

MARTA. It's a holiday for everyone.

KATRINKA. We're very lucky to have a festival this year. I

never thought we would . . . with everybody in the kingdom so sad.

LISA. And the king so worried about his daughters! I never thought he'd let us have a festival. I didn't think we'd ever have a festival again.

GRETCHEN. Not until somebody found out the secret of the worn-out shoes.

FREDA. What do you suppose the secret is, Katrinka? What do you suppose happens?

MARTA. I wish I knew. I'd go right to the palace and tell the king.

KATRINKA. Nobody knows, Freda. All anybody knows is that eight princes have tried to find out and they just disappeared.

FREDA. What do you suppose happened to them?

KATRINKA. Nobody knows. They just vanished.

SARA. Where do you suppose they went to?

LISA. Don't! It makes me shiver. (*In the distance a* BOY'S VOICE *is heard giving a yodeling call. The* LITTLE GIRLS *listen in surprise, spring to their feet.*)

MICHAEL (*off*). Rale-o-ho-ho. Rale-o-ho-ho . . . see my sheep go!

ALL (*ad lib.*). That's Michael! It's Michael.

MARITJE. Michael never comes down from the mountains.

FREDA. Michael tends his sheep all day.

HEDJE. And watches the stars all night.

LISA. Michael wouldn't ever come to a festival.

HEIDI. He doesn't care about girls.

MARITJE. I bet Michael doesn't even know how to dance.

SARA. He looks as if he did.

LISA. I'd like to dance with Michael.

MICHAEL (*off*). Rale-o-ho-ho. . . . See my sheep go. . . .

Down from the green hills! Down from the green hills.

HEDJE. What's Michael doing in the village so early in the day?

MARTA. He should be up on the hills tending his sheep.

ALL. Whatever can be the reason? (MICHAEL *enters. He is a handsome shepherd boy with the eyes of a dreamer, but alert and full of vitality. He wears a bunch of mountain flowers in his hat.*)

GIRLS (*ad lib.*). Michael! What are you doing here? Where are your sheep? Won't your master be angry?

MICHAEL. I've shut up the sheep in the byre. My master told me I could. I've come to the festival. Isn't it time for it to begin? (*The* LITTLE GIRLS *surround him, all talking at once.*)

GIRLS. Michael's come to the festival.

FREDA. Who are you going to dance with tonight at the festival?

HEIDI. Will you dance with me?

KATRINKA. Dance with me, Michael.

HEDJE. No, I want him to dance with me.

LISA. No, with me.

ALL. Everybody wants to dance with Michael. (MICHAEL *breaks away from crowd, crosses to well bench.*)

MICHAEL. I'm not going to dance with any of you.

ALL. Oh! Why not?

MICHAEL. I don't know how to do your kind of dancing.

FREDA. Then we'll show you. It's easy, really it is. Come on and try it, anyway. (*They pull him to C, group around him and do*

Peasant Dance,

a traditional folk-dance with stamping and circling, but woven around the thread of invitation to MICHAEL *to join them and his refusal. When it is over . . .*)

MARTA. I think you're mean, Michael. Why won't you dance with us?

MICHAEL. I tell you, it's not my kind of dancing. Fiddles scraping, heavy boots stamping, everybody doing just what everybody else does. I couldn't do it.

SARA, LISA. But everybody dances at a festival.

MARITJE. I bet he doesn't know how to dance at all. And he's scared to say so.

GRETCHEN. If you're not going to dance, why did you come to the festival?

MICHAEL. I came because the Lady of the Stars told me to.

KATRINKA. Lady of the Stars! Who's that?

GIRLS (ad lib.). Lady of the Stars! Who's she? I never heard of her.

HEIDI. I bet she's somebody you made up.

FREDA. I bet you dreamed it.

MICHAEL. I don't know if it was a dream or not. It was one clear, still night on the mountainside, when the stars were so close it seemed as if you could reach out and touch them. And suddenly she was there, a beautiful lady, all shining and shimmery, as if she had a hundred stars hidden in her dress. She talked to me. She said, "Michael, you have always dreamed of seeing a princess. Go down to the festival in the village and you will find her there. Go down to the festival and you will see your princess."

ALL. A princess!

MARITJE, LISA, GRETCHEN. But there aren't any princesses in our village!

FREDA. There's only us.

HEIDI. And maybe some gypsies!

HEDJE. What would a princess be doing in our village?

MICHAEL. I don't know, but that's what the Lady of the Stars told me.

GRETCHEN. Well, I think the whole thing's silly!

MARITJE. Dreaming about princesses!

FREDA. Coming to a festival and not dancing!

MICHAEL. But imagine dancing with a princess. I've always dreamed of that. She would move so lightly and freely that she wouldn't even crush the petals of the mountain flowers.

HEDJE. Where would you find a princess in our village?

MARITJE. Maybe she's hidden in the well! (*They all laugh.*)

MARTA. Are you going to sit right there by the well and wait for her to come out, Michael, or are you going to have some fun? You're going to see the gypsies dance, aren't you?

MICHAEL. Are gypsies coming to the village?

KATRINKA. They certainly are, and if they're the same ones who came last year they're wonderful dancers—

HEIDI. And they have dark faces, and white teeth, and it makes your feet tap to listen to their tambourine—

MARITJE. —and Lisa's afraid of them!

LISA. Well, I'm not afraid of all of them—only that old woman—

SARA. Her face is all hidden in a long silk scarf—

FREDA. —and my brother saw them last week in the village beyond the mountain, and he says she tells fortunes, and if you cross her palm with silver—

KATRINKA. But she's nobody to be really afraid of, Lisa. What could she do to you?

LISA. Well, my mother says to beware of old gypsy women; they might be witches or bad fairies, and they might cast a spell on you with their eyes—

HEDJE (*half convinced*). I saw her last year, but I never did see her eyes—

LISA. And you mustn't ever buy a ring from an old gypsy woman, or a bracelet, or anything else that goes round you, like a belt, because it might be a magic circle, and then she'd have you in her power, and you wouldn't know what you might do—

SARA (*frightened*). Oh, Lisa!

GRETCHEN. Oh, Lisa, is it all true?

KATRINKA. Well, I don't believe it! Somebody's been telling you stories to frighten you, Lisa.

LISA. My mother said it. And she didn't say it to me; she said it to my big sister when they were sitting around the fire at night, and she didn't know I was listening.

FREDA. O-oh! (*They are all impressed, in spite of themselves, even* KATRINKA—*all but* MICHAEL. FREDA *looks uneasily over her shoulder, and sees the* PRINCESS CELESTINA, *who has just entered. She is the eldest princess—proud, haughty, elegant.* FREDA's "Oh" *changes in tone to one of surprise. The* LITTLE GIRLS *all turn, and stand open-mouthed.* CELESTINA *turns, with an expression of annoyance, and walks upstage, where she stands for a moment gazing off, as if looking for someone.*)

GRETCHEN. Who is she, do you think?

KATRINKA. She has a crown on her head!

MARTA. She must be a princess!

SARA. Then Michael was right!

HEDJE. He did come to our village and see a princess!

MICHAEL (*looking at the* PRINCESS *and obviously disappointed*). That isn't what I thought a princess would be like. (*The* PRINCESS *turns again, sharply, and comes down to them.*)

CELESTINA. Little girls, have any of you seen an old gypsy woman pass this way? A bent old woman who wears a long scarf about her face? (*A whisper runs across the* LITTLE GIRLS—"*an old gypsy woman—*", "*with her head wrapped up in a scarf*"—*but no one answers.*) Well, speak up! Have you lost your tongues? You, child, have you seen her?

FREDA (*who is nearest*). We haven't seen her, miss, but we were just talking about her, and—

CELESTINA. Curtsy when you speak to me and always say "Highness" to a princess. Well? (*But* FREDA *is now so embarrassed that she can do nothing but gulp.*)

KATRINKA (*stepping forward*). Please excuse her, Highness; you frightened her. We haven't seen the old woman, but Freda's brother says she's coming over the mountain when the rest of the gypsies come to the festival.

CELESTINA (*impatiently*). Oh, I know she's coming. She ought to be here now. She's late. Will one of you go and find her for me? She must be in the village somewhere. (*The wave of fear goes over the* LITTLE GIRLS *again, and then* MICHAEL *steps forward.*)

MICHAEL. I will go and fetch her for Your Highness. I'm not afraid of an old woman in a shawl.

CELESTINA. Tell her the Princess Celestina is waiting, and cannot wait long. (MICHAEL *goes.* CELESTINA *paces up and down; the* LITTLE GIRLS *watch her furtively.*)

HEIDI. She isn't very polite, for a princess. She was horrid to Freda.

GRETCHEN. Princesses don't have to be polite, silly. They just tell people what to do, and they don't have to say "please."

SARA. Michael wasn't scared of her, not a bit.

VOICE (*off, in the distance*). Hedje.

HEDJE. That sounds like my mother's voice!

VOICE (off). Maritje!

MARITJE. And that's mine!

VOICE (off). Freda?

FREDA. That's my mother's voice, too!

VOICE (off). Gretchen!

GRETCHEN. And mine.

VOICE (off). Katrinka!

KATRINKA. I guess it's time to cook breakfast.

VOICE (off). Heidi!

HEIDI. I hope she isn't cross.

VOICE (off). Marta!

MARTA. I hope we're not late!

VOICE (off). Lisa!

LISA. That sounds like my mother, too!

VOICE (off). Sara!

SARA. I'm sure that's my mother!

ALL. I guess we'd better go. (*They pick up their jars and exit L, singing their chant.* CELESTINA *comes D, stands looking off after the* GIRLS. *The* OLD GYPSY WOMAN *comes slowly on stage from R, and in a voice that imitates the cadence of the mothers', calls, "Celestina," "Princess Celestina.")*

CELESTINA (*to herself*). Did someone call me? (*Turns slowly, sees* OLD WOMAN.) Oh, it's you.

OLD WOMAN. Didn't you expect me?

CELESTINA. Yes, I sent the boy to find you. It's just that you came so quietly, like—like—

OLD WOMAN. Like magic, you were going to say? Well? Like the message you found under your pillow this morning, telling you to meet me here?

CELESTINA. I was afraid I wouldn't find you before my father and my sisters arrived. They may be here at any minute. Speak quickly. What do you have to say to me?

OLD WOMAN. Hoity-toity! Not so fast, my proud one. All in good time, all in good time—do you have the ring?

CELESTINA (*touching it with her other hand*). Yes, always. It never leaves my finger.

OLD WOMAN (*chuckling*). Good, good. And have you used the power it brought you, as I showed you how to do?

CELESTINA. Yes—my sisters do whatever I command. The charm works exactly as you said it would—one turn, and they are free of the world, in a magic trance where they cannot help but do my bidding—two turns, and they begin to dance—three turns—

OLD WOMAN. Sh! These are secret matters. It is not safe even to whisper them here in the market place. Remember, if the secret were discovered, even now the plan might fail.

CELESTINA. How could anyone discover it? Already eight princes have tried and failed. Eight foolish young men have come begging for my hand in marriage, and not one has been there the next morning to tell my father the secret of the worn-out shoes. They, too, have done exactly as I commanded, and no one but you and I know what has become of them.

OLD WOMAN. Good, good. Then you are satisfied with my magic, Princess? The ring has made you happy?

CELESTINA. My sister Lina is troublesome even now when I have the ring. She struggles against it, and sometimes I am afraid—

OLD WOMAN. What? The little one, with the face like milk? Pah! She is no match for you.

CELESTINA. She seems gentle, but she is different from any of the others. They grow weaker every day, but Lina—

OLD WOMAN. Pah! You are weak, yourself, my fine lady. Have you not learned that in that ring lie all the powers of fear? Threaten your sister—make her look into your eyes as you turn the ring. You say your other sisters will obey you— get them to help you. Let them frighten her, and sneer at her, and laugh at her, until she comes crawling to your feet, mewing like a frightened kitten.

CELESTINA (*frightened in her turn*). Why—why—how dare you speak to me that way? Who are you?

OLD WOMAN (*cringing again*). Forgive me, Princess. For a moment I forgot myself, thinking of the full power that shall be yours some day. For that is what I came to tell you. The time is coming soon when you will fear your sister no longer—when neither she nor anyone else can struggle against you.

CELESTINA. When will it be—tell me—

OLD WOMAN. When the ninth man has tried to find out the secret of the worn-out shoes, when you have conquered him and he disappears, as all the others have done—then the spell will be sealed—then your power will last forever.

CELESTINA. Forever! (*The sound of a tambourine is heard off.*)

OLD WOMAN. Ah, here come my friends. Farewell, Princess. Remember, once more, and the spell is forever.

CELESTINA (*to herself*). Forever. (*Enter the* GYPSIES, *running, dancing, laughing, followed by the* LITTLE GIRLS *and* MICHAEL. *The* GYPSIES *go at once into the*

Gypsy Dance

and when finished, the LITTLE GIRLS *clap delightedly and talk all at once.*)

KATRINKA. That was lovely! That was the best dancing I ever saw!

HEIDI. I wish I could dance like that. I wish I could stamp and kick as high as that.

MARTA. I wish I had a pair of shiny boots like that. (*Off, a trumpet sounds a fanfare.*)

SARA. What's that? What does it mean? (LITTLE GIRLS *run to look.*)

FREDA. Why, look! It's a man all dressed up in a shiny coat, and he's playing the trumpet.

MARITJE. I know what he is—he's a herald. He's announcing something. (*The* HERALD *enters and* LITTLE GIRLS *fall back, awestruck with admiration. He blows another three blasts.*)

HERALD. Hear ye! Hear ye! People of the village. Your king comes to visit you.

LISA. The king!

HEDJE. Coming to our village!

GRETCHEN. The king is coming to our festival!

HERALD. Followed by his eldest daughter, the Princess Celestina, his other daughters, the Princesses Marietta, Florentina, Lizabetta, Ernestina, Henrietta, Loretta, Paulina and his youngest daughter, the Princess Lina.

HEIDI. The nine princesses! All coming to our village!

MARTA. Do your dance again, gypsies. Do it for the king.

FREDA. No, do a different one. Do the one you did last year, with all the twirls in it.

ALL (*ad lib.*). Yes, do that one. Please do that one. That one was lovely. (*The* GYPSIES *start again, this time a fast dance with twirls, but have hardly done a dozen steps, when the* KING *comes roaring in, followed by the eight other* PRINCESSES. CELESTINA *has previously gone upstage, back of the* fountain, and mingles with them unobtrusively as they enter.)

KING. Stop, stop, I say! Don't you hear me? Do I have to have a heart attack before you do what I say? (A tambourine is still jangling.) And stop that confounded racket, too!

GIRLS (ad lib.). It's the king. But why doesn't he like the dancing? What's he so angry for?

GYPSY MAN. Your pardon, great King, we are but humble gypsies who come to dance at your village festival, to take in the tambourine a few pennies—

KING. Quiet! Stop talking! I guess I know what you are. I guess I know a gypsy when I see one. If it wasn't for gypsies and dancing I'd be a happy man. Don't you know it's against the law for gypsies to dance in my kingdom?

GYPSY. But last year, great King, we dance in market place for people, with clapping, with flowers, with pennies—

KING. Quiet! It's only been against the law since last year. And why? Because it was last year that that old gypsy woman came to the palace and sold my daughter Celestina a gold ring, and from that— Here! Hold on! Wait a minute! I believe that's the very same old creature now! Now, madam, step forward! (The OLD GYPSY shuffles forward, her face still half hidden.) Certainly looks like the same one. Celestina!

CELESTINA (coming forward, on the other side of the KING from the GYPSY). Yes, Father.

KING. Is this the same old woman who sold you that confounded ring you seem to set so much store by?

CELESTINA. Yes, Father.

KING. Have you bought anything else from her?

CELESTINA. No, Father.

KING. Well, that's something to be thankful for. (*Turning back toward the* OLD WOMAN, *who has disappeared.*) Now, Madam, all I've got to say to you is, that if I catch— Goodness gracious me, the old creature is gone! Confound my soul, where has she got to? Here, you, young feller, where did she go? (*The* GYPSY MAN *does not answer.*) Speak up, now, or by the great gold unicorn on the palace roof, I'll—well?

GYPSY MAN. Pardon, great King, but gypsy does not know. Old woman come like little mist of evening—she go like little mist of morning.

KING (*disgusted*). What kind of an answer is that? She come like little mist of— (*To* GIRLS.) You see, that's the way gypsies always talk. Can't make a grain of sense out of them. Well, young man, you and the rest of your friends can stay just long enough to hear what I'm going to say next, and then you'll have to go like a little mist of whatever it is, and do your dancing somewhere else. Now, little girls, I'm sorry to spoil your festival by stopping the dancing, but I do believe all our troubles started with that old woman. And speaking of trouble, let's get down to business. (*Goes to seat.*) All right, now let's have the Proclamation. I want all of you to listen very carefully. This is important, and I don't want you to miss one word.

HERALD. Hear ye! Hear ye! Let it be proclaimed in every village from the mountains to the seashore—let it be proclaimed on the first day of May—that a reward will be presented to any young man who will discover the secret of the princesses' worn-out shoes.

LITTLE GIRLS. The princesses' worn-out shoes!

HERALD. I, the King of this country . . .

KING (*rising, and coming down to the* LITTLE GIRLS). That

means me, really. I'm giving this proclamation, but I have him do it for me, because he can make more noise than I can. (*Continues to talk to some of the* LITTLE GIRLS *in pantomime, as* MICHAEL *comes down on the other side of the stage, and speaks to the* LITTLE GIRLS *near him.*)

MICHAEL. It's happening just as my Lady of the Stars said it would. She said for me to come to the village and I would see a princess.

GIRLS. It's just like Michael's dream!

MICHAEL. She said I would see a princess. (*Looking at the* PRINCESS LINA, *who rises slowly to her feet.*)

LINA. Boy, why do you look at me so?

MICHAEL. Princess— (*Reaches for his bouquet of flowers, starts to give them to her.*)

CELESTINA (*also rising*). What's this? Lina, what are you doing?

LINA. Nothing, Celestina. (MICHAEL RETIRES.)

CELESTINA. I don't like it.

KING (*coming back to his seat*). Now, now, daughters, no bickering on May Day. (*To* HERALD.) Proceed.

HERALD. I, the King of this country, proclaim that, though my daughters are shut up in their bedroom every night, and the door triple-locked upon them, in the morning their satin shoes are worn through.

KING. You understand what that means, do you? (LITTLE GIRLS *nod.*) Every night those girls are shut up in their rooms with brand new satin slippers, and the next morning, there are those shoes with holes . . . holes, you understand. (*Picks up* LINA's *foot, taps on the sole of her shoe.*) Right through the bottom . . . as if they'd danced all night long! I tell you I'm worried about this. I don't know where they go or what they do.

HERALD. I, the King, proclaim that to any young man, who- ever he be, who discovers the secret of the worn-out shoes, I will give the hand of any one of my daughters in mar- riage.

PRINCESSES (*ad lib.*). No, Father, no!

CELESTINA. None of us could marry anyone but a prince!

KING. Nonsense. Eight princes have tried already to find out the secret, and they all failed. Each one was supposed to watch outside your door at night. And what happened? They disappeared. Now, you, Celestina, I'll have no objec- tions from you. You were the one who said that none of your sisters could marry till you did. Well, that's all right . . . and I was willing to stand by it, if you insisted. But your eight princes disappeared, and now where are you? (*To* LITTLE GIRLS.) I tell you, they just vanished. You understand? (LITTLE GIRLS *nod.* KING *turns back to* CELES- TINA.) This thing is enough to drive any father crazy. So I'm not going to worry any more whether it's a prince or not, or who gets married first. Now I offer the hand of any one of my daughters in marriage to any young man who can find out the secret.

PRINCESSES. Oh, Father!

FLORENTINA. He might be a cobbler!

MARIETTA. He might be a farmer!

LIZABETTA. He might be a blacksmith!

CELESTINA. He might be a peasant!

KING. Quiet, all of you! (*To* CELESTINA.) I must find out why you dance all night, if that's what you do. I don't think you know yourselves what you do, or why you do it. Do you? Celestina, do you? (CELESTINA *is backing away from him during this attack.*) I don't believe you know why you dance all night. Is that really what you do? Celestina, is it?

(CELESTINA *turns her back on him and, as though in an involuntary attempt to escape the questioning, turns the ring once on her finger. The* KING, *getting no answer, turns back, and sees the* PRINCESSES, *who, at the first turn of the ring, have come forward into position, gazing straight ahead as if hypnotized. As* CELESTINA *turns the ring the second time, the* PRINCESSES *cross each other, turn, and curtsy.* KING *booms—*) There! You see! (CELESTINA'S *hand drops.* PRINCESSES *start and return to their places.*) Something happened to them. They looked as if they weren't in this world. That's the sort of thing that goes on all the time. Act as if they were in a dream—as if they were under some kind of a spell.

SARA. Oh, Lisa!

LISA. You see, Sara, it is a magic ring.

SARA. Your mother was right.

LISA. My mother's always right.

KING (*to* HERALD). All right, now you can go on with the proclamation.

HERALD. But it's all over, Sire. That's all there is to it.

KING. Oh, it is? Well, then I guess our business is done. Does everybody understand?

LITTLE GIRLS, GYPSIES. Yes, Your Majesty.

KING. Well, I guess I can be moving on. I have to make this proclamation in every village in my kingdom between now and next Tuesday. Go on and have the rest of your festival—everybody have a good time. Come on, Celestina, Marietta, Florentina, Lizabetta, Ernestina, Henrietta, Paulina, Lauretta, Lina!

PRINCESSES. Yes, Father; coming, Father.

KING. Good-bye, little girls, good-bye. (*Waves to the* LITTLE

GIRLS, *motions to the* HERALD *to lead off the royal party, which he does, blowing his trumpet.*)

GIRLS (*following to exit*). Good-bye, Your Majesty, good-bye. Good-bye, Your Highnesses.

MARTA. Let's go down the street and watch them go.

HEDJE. Let's do.

HEIDI. It isn't every day that the king comes to our village. (GIRLS *run off after him and* GYPSIES *fade away.* MICHAEL *is left alone. From the time that the* PRINCESS LINA *and the others danced to the magic of the ring,* MICHAEL *has never taken his eyes off her, and now stands looking after her. Slowly he takes the flowers from his hat, practices kneeling and presenting the flowers to her. Then he pretends to take her hand, and lead her into a dance with him. As he plays this out, the lights have been changing to a soft half-twilight, and the* LADY OF THE STARS *enters behind him, passes her wand through the air, and* MICHAEL *stops, passes his hand over his eyes as if he were suddenly very sleepy, half stumbles to the well bench, sinks down over-come with sleep. The* LADY *comes nearer, looks at him, straightens in satisfaction, then steps back and calls.*)

LADY OF THE STARS. Michael! Michael! Michael!

MICHAEL (*half sitting up*). Who is calling me?

LADY OF THE STARS. It is I, Michael. Your Lady of the Stars.

MICHAEL (*his eyes open now*). Oh! You're so shining and shimmery I can hardly see you. Why have you come to me again?

LADY OF THE STARS. Michael, I have come to tell you that you have been chosen to discover the secret of the worn-out shoes.

MICHAEL. I shall discover the secret of the worn-out shoes! But how can I?

LADY OF THE STARS. You must go to the palace and take service as a gardener's boy. The first command that will be laid on you will be to have ready each morning nine bouquets, and to present one to each of the nine princesses. In that way you will see the princesses every day.

MICHAEL. I shall see the Princess Lina every day. The Princess Lina is just what I imagined a princess would be—as delicate and dainty as mayflowers in the forest—

LADY OF THE STARS. The Princess Lina is in danger, Michael. Are you brave enough to save her from the terrible fate that hangs over her? If you are, your reward shall be to marry her—Michael, the gardener's boy, shall marry a princess.

MICHAEL. But a gardener's boy couldn't marry a princess any more than a shepherd could!

LADY OF THE STARS. The king's proclamation said that any young man may try to discover the secret of the worn-out shoes. And I have brought you a present to help you. (*She holds out two little laurel trees in pots, which she takes from a silvery basket. Delighted, he takes them and carries them to the bench.*)

MICHAEL. Oh! Two little laurel trees! A cherry laurel and a rose laurel! They're beautiful.

LADY OF THE STARS. You must take your little laurels to the palace and plant them in two large pots. Now, here is a little silver rake, a golden watering-pot, and a silken towel. (*Holding each up from the basket.*) Every day you must rake the laurels with the rake, water them with the watering-pot, and wipe their leaves with the towel. When they have grown as tall as a girl of fifteen, say to both of them, "My beautiful laurels, with this silver rake I have raked you, with this golden watering-pot I have watered you, and with this silken towel I have wiped your leaves." Then the laurels will help you to find the secret.

MICHAEL. Oh, Lady of the Stars, how can I ever thank you? Surely with their help I can discover the reason for the worn-out shoes. But whose secret is it?

LADY OF THE STARS. That I cannot tell you. I have only been allowed to come and help you now because this is the last chance to save the Princess Lina from the dreadful doom that threatens her.

MICHAEL. Why have the stars chosen a poor shepherd boy, when the world is full of soldiers and gentlemen and princes who are richer and handsomer and stronger than I?

LADY OF THE STARS. You have been chosen, Michael, because you are brave and free. And if you are brave enough, she may yet be saved, but if you should fail, her doom is sealed forever. You must risk your own life, if the Princess Lina is ever to walk again in the sunlight of freedom.

MICHAEL. I would gladly risk my life to save the Princess Lina. Only tell me what I must do to save her!

LADY OF THE STARS. All I can tell you is that you must brave the power of the Princess Celestina's ring . . . you must move through the terrible dances of death. . . .

MICHAEL. I am not afraid of the Princess Celestina, or the magic ring, or of any death a man might die—

LADY OF THE STARS. Most difficult of all, Michael, you must help the Princess Lina to free herself. You must teach her to dance as you do, Michael. I have seen you dancing by yourself on the mountainside, when you thought you were all alone. Teach her to dance as the free things of the world dance; to bend and dip like the long grass when a little wind runs over the mountain, to sway like the trees on the road to the village when a storm is coming, to run and leap like your little goats when the sun is warm on the mountain pastures. Teach her how the stars dance on a frosty night when you wrap yourself in your cloak and watch them and imagine that you see princesses dancing. (*During this speech* MICHAEL *has begun to move, and now starts to dance.*)

MICHAEL. I can teach her to dance like that—to bend like the grass.

LADY OF THE STARS. —to sway like the trees—to run as lightly as the goats—

MICHAEL. I will teach her to dance as the stars dance— Oh— Star Lady, where have you gone?

LADY OF THE STARS (*fading*). Remember, Michael, most difficult of all—help the Princess Lina to free herself—(*fading*) to free herself—

MICHAEL. Don't go away now—come back and tell me more—

LADY OF THE STARS (*off*). I can tell you no more. Find out the secret of the worn-out shoes and you shall marry the princess— (MICHAEL *rushes to look in several directions, then realizes she is really gone. Goes back to bench, where he falls asleep, suddenly rubs his eyes, pinches himself to see if he was dreaming, sees the laurels, picks one up, smiles in the knowledge that it really happened.*)

LINA (*off*). Boy! Shepherd boy! (*Coming on.*) Oh! You're still here!

MICHAEL. Princess!

LINA. I—I lost the little silver clasp that I wear in my hair.

MICHAEL. I'll help you find it. (*Begins to look around well.*)

LINA. What is your name, boy?

MICHAEL. Michael. (*They search some more, stealing glances at each other.)* It isn't here, Princess. But here are some flowers that I picked for you when I came down the mountain this morning. Maybe you could wear these in your hair instead.

LINA. Oh, they're beautiful! The colors are so bright, and the petals are so delicate.

MICHAEL. There were hundreds of them all over the mountain. They shone so, with the dew on them, they looked like little colored stars.

LINA. I'll wear them in my hair, and remember that you gave them to me.

MICHAEL. I'll bring you flowers every morning, Princess, because I'm coming to the palace to take service as a gardener's boy.

LINA. Coming to the palace! Why?

MICHAEL. I'm really coming to discover the secret of the worn-out shoes.

LINA. Oh, no, Michael, you mustn't. Something dreadful will happen to you. I'm afraid for you.

MICHAEL. I am not afraid for myself, Princess. And you must be brave, too, if I am to save you from— Little Princess!

LINA. Yes, Michael, why did you stop so suddenly?

MICHAEL. Little Princess, will you grant me a great favor? *(Drops on one knee.)*

LINA. Oh, yes, Michael, but you don't need to kneel for it. I like it better when you stand—and look into my eyes.

MICHAEL. Will you dance for me, Princess? All my life I have dreamed of seeing a princess dance.

LINA. I'll dance if you want me to, Michael, because I like you, and you make me feel happy and strong, as I haven't felt for a long time. *(Troubled.)* I don't really like to dance—but I'll dance for you, Michael. I'll show you how we dance at court.

LINA's *Solo*

(In it she expresses the stilted elegance of a court dance, and at the same time some rebellion against it. Her face has a sad, masklike quality. When the dance ends MICHAEL *says nothing.)* Well, Michael, did you like my dance?

MICHAEL. It was beautiful, Princess, but it wasn't a happy dance. It's not the kind of dancing I thought it would be at all.

LINA. But what other kind is there?

MICHAEL. I wish I could show you how I dance in the mountains.

LINA. Show me, Michael! I've never known any dances but the ones at court.

MICHAEL. Maybe you could learn to dance happily. But you must think of free things. Of the wind in your hair as you run—of the mountain brooks laughing over stones—

LINA *(catching it).* —of flowers—and sunshine—

MICHAEL. —and stars— *(He begins to dance.* LINA *is watching him, half moving as he does, her face lighting up.* CELESTINA *enters, stops short as she see* MICHAEL.*)*

CELESTINA. What wild capering is this? *(Catching sight of* LINA.*)* Lina! What are you doing here, watching this rough boy?

LINA. He's showing me a new kind of dancing.

CELESTINA. Dancing! Is that what you call it? I thought you were looking for your silver clasp.

LINA. I—I am, Celestina. It was just about here that I lost it.

CELESTINA. And will watching a shepherd boy help you find

it? For shame! Can't you remember that you are a princess?

LINA. But, Celestina, he was showing me how they dance in the mountains. It was beautiful.

CELESTINA. Beautiful! You must have lost your senses.

LINA. Well, it was strange and different. But I want to see more— I—if he will dance again.

MICHAEL. Oh, yes, Princess, gladly.

CELESTINA (*ignoring* MICHAEL). You little fool! (*Begins to raise her hand with the ring.*)

LINA (*staring in terror at the ring*). No, no, Celestina, please—

CELESTINA. Very well, then. Are you coming?

LINA. Yes, Celestina. I'm coming. (CELESTINA *exits and* LINA *follows, but runs back.*) Don't come to the palace, Michael. I'm afraid for you. Don't—please!

CELESTINA (*off*). Lina!

MICHAEL. I am coming, Princess. I must!

CURTAIN

ACT TWO

SCENE: *The Princesses' dressing room. A door R opens into the palace corridor, a door L opens into the Princesses' bedroom. Nine dainty dressing tables and stools, exactly alike, are placed at regular intervals upstage. The laurel trees, as tall as Lina, are in decorative pots, one R and one L at the side walls. The stage is lit with early morning sunlight.*

At the rise of the curtain the stage is empty. Then from the bedroom enter ERNESTINA, HENRIETTA, LORETTA, *stretching sleepily, the down sweep of their stretch carrying them*

into position with a half run or swoop, ERNESTINA *DR,* HEN-
RIETTA *DRC,* LORETTA *DL. They end movement with a
sleepy "Oh."* PAULINA, LIZABETTA, LINA *enter, rubbing their
eyes and reach position on a line with others,* PAULINA *L of*
ERNESTINA, LIZABETTA *L of* HENRIETTA, LINA *L of* LORETTA.
They end movement with a sleepy "Oh" in a different tone.
MARIETTA, CELESTINA, FLORENTINA *enter, yawning and pat-
ting their mouths, reach positions R, C, L, respectively, above
the others, thus forming the apexes of three triangles. Their
"Oh" is in still another tone.*

ERNESTINA, HENRIETTA, LORETTA. It's morning again. (*Drop
their heads on shoulders of* MARIETTA, CELESTINA, FLOREN-
TINA.)

PAULINA, LIZABETTA, LINA. The sun is shining in the windows.
(*Put their hands over their eyes.*)

MARIETTA, CELESTINA, FLORENTINA. It's time to get up!

PAULINA. But I don't want to get up. (*Snuggles on* MARI-
ETTA's *shoulder.*)

LIZABETTA. I just want to put my head under the covers and
sleep till noon. (*Snuggles on* CELESTINA's *shoulder.*)

LINA. Why did we have to dance all night? (*Snuggles on*
FLORENTINA's *shoulder.*)

ERNESTINA. It's delicious to dance all night.

HENRIETTA. But I want to sleep all day.

LORETTA. Let's go back to bed!

ALL (*but* CELESTINA). Yes, let's! (*Start moving in character.*)

CELESTINA (*clapping hands*). Stop! (ALL *stop.*) Silly creatures!
Come back at once.

SEVERAL (*protesting*). Oh, Celestina.

CELESTINA. Back at once, I say! It's time to be up.

OTHERS (*resigned*). Yes, Celestina. (ALL *come back and slump* down; MARIETTA and FLORENTINA on *dressing table stools;* ERNESTINA and PAULINA on *the floor either side of* MARI-ETTA, *each with elbow and head on* MARIETTA'S *knees;* LORETTA and LINA *same positions in relation to* FLOREN-TINA; HENRIETTA and LIZABETTA on *floor, elbows on knees, chins in hands.*)

CELESTINA. You can't sleep all day. Don't you know you have things to do?

ALL. Yes, Celestina.

CELESTINA. Don't you remember this is the day you are to have your new ball dresses fitted?

MARIETTA, FLORENTINA. Our ball dresses!

ALL (*but* CELESTINA *and* LINA). We are going to have new ball dresses!

LINA. What do we want new ones for?

ALL. Oh, Lina!

LINA. Well, I don't want a new ball dress. (*Rising.*) I don't care if I never have another ball dress as long as I live!

ALL (*shocked*). Oh, Lina!

LORETTA, PAULINA. We only have twenty.

HENRIETTA, ERNESTINA, LIZABETTA. We only have fifty.

MARIETTA, FLORENTINA. We only have a hundred!

ALL (*but* CELESTINA *and* LINA). We do need new ball dresses!

CELESTINA. And just as we do every morning, we must choose new pairs of dancing shoes.

ALL (*but* CELESTINA *and* LINA). That's right!

HENRIETTA, LIZABETTA. We wore out another pair of shoes last night.

MARIETTA, FLORENTINA. We danced right through the soles of them!

PAULINA, LORETTA. What will Father say?

CELESTINA. Father won't say a thing, as you know perfectly well.

ERNESTINA (*rising*). Oh, yes, he will. I know just what he'll say. (*Imitating him.*) Nine new pairs of shoes! What's the world coming to? What am I coming to? The poorhouse, that's what I'm coming to. Have to raise taxes. Have to sell the palace! What's the matter with all the young men? Why doesn't somebody discover the secret—

LINA (*to* ERNESTINA). Well, I'm going to tell him the secret. I'm going right to him and tell him how we dance all night. I'm going to tell him the whole secret!

ALL. Lina, you wouldn't!

LINA. Yes, I would.

CELESTINA. Oh, no, she wouldn't. Don't worry about Lina. Lina gets these ideas, but she soon realizes how foolish they are, don't you, Lina? At the May festival she ran away from us to talk to a common shepherd boy, didn't you, Lina?

LINA. Yes, I did, and I—

CELESTINA. And you came away when I told you to, didn't you, Lina? Do you want me to stop you when you run to Father, now, little sister? (*Raises hand with ring.*)

LINA. No, Celestina—I—

CELESTINA. Don't bother about Lina, girls. Hurry now. We must say good morning to Father.

ALL. We haven't said good morning to Father!

HENRIETTA, LIZABETTA. We almost forgot.

PAULINA, LORETTA. But, Celestina—

MARIETTA. We can't say good morning to Father yet.

FLORENTINA. We don't have our bouquets.

LINA. We never say good morning to Father without our bouquets.

MARIETTA, FLORENTINA. We'll have to wait.

CELESTINA. What a nuisance. Perhaps all the servants are sleeping late. Loretta, see if the seamstresses are at work. (LORETTA *runs to bedroom door and opens it.*) Yes, they're here. They're laying out our new ball gowns. One's rose. (ALL *but* CELESTINA *and* LINA *run to look.*)

MARIETTA. That's mine.

HENRIETTA. One's yellow.

FLORENTINA. And one's blue.

LORETTA. And they're unpacking dozens of pairs of shoes.

CELESTINA (*clapping hands*). That's enough. Close the door. Don't interrupt them with your silly chatter. At least they are on time with their work. What's the matter with that stupid boy? He ought to have been here long ago.

LINA. He's not stupid, Celestina. He's the best gardener's boy we ever had.

HENRIETTA. Nobody ever brought us such lovely flowers.

LIZABETTA (*giggling*). I think the flowers grow just to please him.

MARIETTA. Really, Lizabetta.

PAULINA. If it wasn't for the gardener's boy, Celestina, we shouldn't have these lovely laurels to decorate our dressing room and make it bright.

CELESTINA. They are handsome plants, I grant you. Otherwise, I would never have had them brought in from the garden.

LINA. The gardener's boy brought them from his own village.

LORETTA. See how their leaves shine—

HENRIETTA. Just like satin—

LINA. No wonder they shine. He wipes them every day with a little silken towel.

ERNESTINA. Oh, he does, does he? Well, Lina seems to know a great deal about the gardener's boy and his laurel trees. What does he do, Lina, tell you all his secrets?

MARIETTA. I should think that would be the most dreadful nuisance. (*There are three knocks at the door.*)

THREE PRINCESSES. Listen to that. (*Three more knocks.*)

THREE OTHERS. That's the gardener's boy now. (*Three more knocks.*)

THREE OTHERS. At last!

CELESTINA. Come in, gardener's boy. (*Enter* MICHAEL *from corridor, carrying flat garden basket with nine small conventional bouquets and his magic garden tools. He gives bouquets to* PRINCESSES *in order of their age, each reacting in character. With background music, the movement could constitute a near dance,* MICHAEL *mocking the formal court bow with his exaggeration, the* PRINCESSES *not recognizing his mockery.*)

MICHAEL. Good morning, Highness. I have brought your flowers from the garden.

CELESTINA. And you are fifteen minutes late with them, boy. See that it doesn't happen again.

MICHAEL (*to* MARIETTA). Your flowers from the garden, Princess.

MARIETTA. And very nice, too, boy. You really have a knack with them.

MICHAEL. Flowers from the garden, Princess Florentina.

FLORENTINA. Yes, very nice indeed. But late, as my sister said.

MICHAEL. Flowers from the garden, Highness.

ERNESTINA. Every bouquet different! You're a clever boy.

MICHAEL. Flowers from the garden, Princess.

PAULINA. Oh, very handsome.

CELESTINA. Paulina!

PAULINA. The flowers, I meant, of course, Celestina.

MICHAEL. This little bouquet is yours, Princess Lizabetta. (*All she does is giggle.*) And this one yours, Highness. (*To* HENRIETTA.)

HENRIETTA. They're lovelier every day, Michael.

MICHAEL. These are yours, Princess.

LORETTA. What are the names of the flowers? Oh! (*As he goes by her without answering and gives* LINA *hers—*)

MICHAEL. I picked these for you, Princess Lina.

LINA. Thank you, Michael. They're beautiful.

LORETTA. He always gives Lina the prettiest bouquet.

HENRIETTA. Nonsense, darling, yours is just as pretty. (PRINCESSES *draw together comparing bouquets,* MICHAEL *and* LINA *unobserved DL.*)

LINA. Oh, Michael, they are the loveliest, but not half as beautiful as the mountain flowers you gave me the day of the festival. Michael, are you homesick for the mountains?

MICHAEL. Yes, Princess. Sometimes I can hardly sleep in my warm bed in the gardener's house, for thinking of the frosty mountain stars and the wind in the hills at dawn. The flowers in the palace garden are delicate and beautiful but I hate to see them growing in rows.

LINA. I hate anything in patterns! I hate to do the same thing day after day, in the same order. But that's the way my sister Celestina wants it.

MICHAEL. Your sister Celestina likes things in patterns.

LINA. Sometimes I wish more than anything in the whole world that I didn't know what was around the corner of the next minute. I want to do things that are unexpected. But Celestina's always angry when I do.

MICHAEL. Like talking to the gardener's boy?

LINA. Oh, Michael, you're right. She'll be angry if she sees us. And I'm so afraid that some day she'll notice that you're the same boy she saw in the village. Your dancing made her so angry. She'd punish you, surely.

MICHAEL. Don't be afraid of that, little Princess. Your sister would never know me because she never looks at the faces of the people who serve her. (CELESTINA *has been lining up the* PRINCESSES *to go to say good morning to the* KING *and now misses* LINA.)

CELESTINA. Lina! Why, where's Lina? (*Turns and sees* MICHAEL *and* LINA.) Lina, what are you doing? Come here this instant.

LINA. Yes, sister. (*Runs to her place in line and waits, terrified.*)

CELESTINA. Dawdling, lazy boy, get on with your work. Tend the laurel trees. But quickly! If you are not gone by the time we return, I'll report you to the gardener for a whipping. We keep no laggards in our service here. (MICHAEL *goes quickly to one of the laurels and begins raking.*) Come, sisters, are you in the proper order? Marietta, Florentina, Lizabetta, Ernestina, Henrietta, Paulina, Loretta and Lina.

PRINCESSES. Yes, Celestina. (*Move to go.*)

CELESTINA (*clapping hands*). Just a minute, Marietta. Have you forgotten that I always go first?

MARIETTA. No, Celestina. (*They exit, led by* CELESTINA. LINA *almost goes out but darts back to* MICHAEL.)

LINA. Oh, Michael, I was so frightened when she spoke to you.

MICHAEL. I told you, Princess, that she would never look at me.

LINA. Michael, if you are homesick for the free mountains, why don't you go back to them?

MICHAEL. I cannot go, Princess. The Lady of the Stars chose me to discover the secret of the worn-out shoes and I must stay until I do.

LINA. But you've been here nearly a month and you haven't tried to discover it.

MICHAEL. I have to wait for the time to come.

LINA. But when will it come, Michael? How will you know?

MICHAEL. When the laurel trees— (*Looks from trees to* LINA *and stops.*) Princess!

LINA. What is it?

MICHAEL. Come and stand beside the tree, Princess. (LINA *does so.*) How old are you, Princess?

LINA. Why, Michael, you know as well as I do. I told you I am fifteen.

MICHAEL. And which is taller, Princess, you or the laurels?

LINA. Why, I am, of course. They couldn't—why, Michael! They have grown much faster than I thought. We are exactly of a height.

MICHAEL. Then the laurel trees are as tall as a girl of fifteen. (*As he speaks a single blossom appears, as if by magic, on each tree, a white one on the* CHERRY LAUREL *and a pink one on the* ROSE LAUREL.)

LINA. O-o-oh, look. They're blossoming all in a second. Almost as if they heard what you said. It's like magic, Michael. As if it meant something special.

MICHAEL. It does mean something. It means that the time has come to discover the secret of the worn-out shoes.

LINA. Oh, no, Michael, no! Something dreadful will happen to you! You'll disappear from the world as all the others did.

MICHAEL. Princess, do you know the secret?

LINA. Oh, Michael, I don't really. None of us can remember in the daytime—except, maybe, Celestina. (*Trying hard to remember.*) There are steps—many steps going down—and fairy woods. Oh, yes, I begin to see one of them now— its trees are covered with diamonds. Of course, we know we dance all night . . . in an enchanted ballroom. But where it is—I don't know. I don't know! Oh, let someone else try to discover the secret!

MICHAEL. You must not be afraid, little Princess. I was chosen because the Lady of the Stars saw me dancing in the mountains and knew that I was a free man, and not afraid.

LINA. Dance for me, Michael. Do your mountain dance— the way you started to do it for me that day in the village. Maybe if I watch you I can learn not to be afraid, too.

MICHAEL. I have been waiting for you to want to learn. Watch me with your eyes and your heart. If you can learn to dance as the free things of the world dance, we can break the wicked spell and you need never again fear the Princess Celestina and her ring.

LINA. —as the free things of the world dance—

MICHAEL's *Solo*

Oh, Michael, it's beautiful! If I could only do it!

MICHAEL. Try it! Remember to think of free things—

LINA. Of the wind in my hair—

MICHAEL (*beginning movement*). Of the mountain brooks—

LINA (*following his movement*). Of flowers and sunshine—

MICHAEL. Now— (*into dance without music,* LINA *following*) to bend like the grass—to sway like the trees—to run as lightly as the goats— (*When he illustrates this with swift* movement, LINA *cannot follow, falters, sinks down in tears.*)

LINA. Oh, Michael, I can't do it! My feet can only follow the court ways that I know. I shall never be able to learn! I will never escape from the ring and my sister Celestina. I shall never be free, or happy, as long as I live.

MICHAEL. Then you must come to the mountains and learn. There you can really feel the wind in your hair. There you can see the little lambs running in the pasture. . . .

LINA. Oh, I know I could learn if I were with you in the mountains. If I could only escape from the palace—

MICHAEL. Oh, beautiful Princess, will you come away to the mountains and marry me? I have loved you ever since I first saw you in my dreams. Come with me and we will break the spell together.

LINA. And I have loved you since you first looked at me. Oh, Michael, I will marry you, and we will run away to the mountains, and I shall never be afraid again! (*Runs to door, turns to him.*) Let's go quickly before Celestina comes looking for me. (*Swings door open, stops in horror.*) Celestina!

CELESTINA (*entering*). So! You will run to the mountains and marry a gardener's boy, will you? You will escape from the palace and your sister, will you? And how will you do it?

LINA. I will just walk out of the palace and go away. I am going to do what I want to do, Celestina. I am never going to be afraid again.

CELESTINA. Have you forgotten the ring, Lina? Have you forgotten what happens when I turn the ring?

LINA. Michael, help me. She's going to turn the ring.

MICHAEL. Don't look at it, Princess. Be strong and don't look at it!

CELESTINA. You may look away, but you will know that I am turning it. There! I have turned the ring once. (LINA *half freezes but reaches out for* MICHAEL.)

LINA. Where are you, Michael?

MICHAEL (*coming forward with hand out*). Here is my hand, Princess.

CELESTINA (*quickly*). I am turning the ring a second time. (*Just as* LINA *is about to take* MICHAEL's *hand the magic works. With her hand a few inches from his, she makes a slow court curtsy, rises, turns her back on him.*)

MICHAEL. Princess!

CELESTINA. Very nice, little sister. And here is a proper partner for you. (LINA *seems to take the hand of an invisible partner and dances a few slow steps.*) And now—(*as* LINA *ends the brief drugged dance*) where are you going, little sister?

LINA. Out—this door—

CELESTINA. And where then, little sister? (LINA *moves toward door.*)

LINA. —going to say—good morning to—Father. (*Exit.*)

CELESTINA (*closing door softly*). There. (*Turns to* MICHAEL.) So, the gardener's boy has decided to marry the princess, has he? For daring even to think such a thing I should have you flogged and thrown in the palace dungeon. But I will be much kinder than you deserve. The Princess Lina is a foolish little girl who forgot her position for a moment. What we must do is send you far, far from the palace. Yes, you must take the road to the east and go as fast as your legs will carry you. At this time tomorrow, if you are within the boundaries of this kingdom, I will have you ridden down and trampled to death by the horses of the guard. Do you understand?

MICHAEL. Yes, Highness, you have given me banishment.

CELESTINA. Or death. It is for you to choose. (*Exit.*)

MICHAEL. I'm not afraid of you or the guard and all its horses. (*Turns and cries out.*) Oh, Lady of the Stars, what can I do? Banished or dead, I cannot help the Princess Lina to break the wicked spell that holds her. I did just as you said. I came to the palace as a gardener's boy. I have tended the laurels. . . . The laurels! (*Quickly picks up tools, speaks, carefully recalling exact words.*) My beautiful laurels (*music begins*), with this silver rake I have raked you. With this golden watering-pot I have watered you. With this silken towel I have wiped your leaves. Now, I beg of you, help me. Give me my wish. (*To the music, the spirits of the trees step out with a few movements indicating returning life.*)

LAURELS. Thank you for bringing us to life. Tell us your wish and we will grant it.

MICHAEL. I want to know the secret of the worn-out shoes.

CHERRY LAUREL. Then you must pluck the white flower from my branches.

MICHAEL (*picking flower*). And what shall I do with it?

CHERRY LAUREL.. You must wear it in your buttonhole, and it will make you invisible. Tonight, when the princesses come to this room, you must steal in with them. They will not be able to see you because of the flower you are wearing. You can follow them wherever they go.

MICHAEL. Invisible! I shall discover the secret of the worn-out shoes! But wait. . . . I cannot tell the secret until after I present myself to the king—as a suitor—and watch outside the princesses' door. What shall I—

ROSE LAUREL. Sh! Listen, Michael! (*From the corridor is heard the faint chatter of the returning* PRINCESSES.)

MICHAEL. The princesses! They are coming back.

CHERRY LAUREL. We can tell you no more now, Michael. We must hide our faces from all but you. (*Both disappear behind trees.* MICHAEL *runs to corridor door, opens it part way. Laughter and talk are clearer but still distant. Runs to bedroom door, opens it but sees seamstresses, closes it quickly. Tries unsuccessfully to hide under dressing table, then behind a laurel. Notices flower in his hand, puts it in buttonhole, tries to look at himself to see if he is invisible. As the talk grows louder in the corridor, sees garden tools, hides them under a dressing table or behind a laurel just as* PRINCESSES *enter. During next few speeches* MICHAEL *shrinks in a corner, not sure he is invisible, becomes bolder as no one notices him, finally passes his hand before the face of one of the* PRINCESSES. *When there is no reaction he is delighted and starts moving to door.*)

LORETTA. —don't know how you knew exactly what he was going to say, Ernestina—

MARIETTA. But, of course, Loretta, poor dear Father always says exactly the same thing—

LIZABETTA (*giggling*). —always the same same thing exactly—

FLORENTINA. —"Nine new pairs of shoes"—just the way you said he would.

HENRIETTA. It really was naughty of you, though, Ernestina, to walk up and down behind him, and do the same thing he was doing. What if poor Father turned around and saw you?

PAULINA. But it was funny!

LIZABETTA (*giggling*). I thought I'd die laughing! (MICHAEL *is tiptoeing to door.*)

CELESTINA. And what if Father went by in the corridor and heard you now? Close the door, Loretta.

LORETTA. Yes, Celestina. (*Shuts it just in time to stop* MICHAEL, *who pantomimes despair.*)

CELESTINA. It's all very well to laugh, Lizabetta, but you wouldn't laugh if Father put you on bread and water for three days, or shut you up in the dungeon with toads and snakes. (MICHAEL, *seeing them engrossed in conversation, creeps up and starts opening door.*)

LIZABETTA. Oh! Toads and snakes!

PAULINA. He wouldn't do it, Celestina.

CELESTINA. Don't be too sure.

LORETTA. Oh, Celestina, you're frightening me!

HENRIETTA. You're really frightening her, Celestina.

CELESTINA. Well, maybe it will teach her respect for her elders, and obedience—and speaking of obedience, I thought I told you to close that door, Loretta. (MICHAEL, *who has door half open, freezes.*)

LORETTA. Well, I did close it, Celestina.

CELESTINA. With your usual carelessness, evidently. It's open, now.

FLORENTINA. I'll close it. Then we'll know it's done. (*Swiftly shuts it,* MICHAEL *hurriedly backing away. As* FLORENTINA *returns to group,* MICHAEL *starts one more attempt.*)

LIZABETTA. Do it once more, Ernestina, the way you did it this morning. I'll pretend that I'm Father, and you do what you did this morning. (LIZABETTA *paces up and down, gesturing, like the King,* ERNESTINA *following her with exaggerated mimicry. All but* CELESTINA *and* LINA *are laughing when* LORETTA *catches sight of the open door.*)

LORETTA. O-o-oh! Look! The door's open again. It's magic. I knew I closed it before. It just opens by magic.

CELESTINA. Magic! Nonsense. There's probably a draft from the corridor. (*She strides to the door,* MICHAEL *pulling away in time. A ruffle on her skirt catches and is torn as she shuts the door.*)

LORETTA (*as* CELESTINA *disengages the ruffle and examines it*). Look at the ruffle on Celestina's dress—it's all torn. Oh, Celestina, I believe that's magic, too.

CELESTINA. Why should there be magic in a door? Loretta, come and stand right in front of this door.

LORETTA (*obeying reluctantly*). Oh, Celestina.

CELESTINA. Stay right there. You'll see there is no magic and that may put some sense in your addled pate. (MICHAEL, *seeing he is trapped, accepts the situation and seizes his chance to make fun of* CELESTINA.) Henrietta, go and get pins from the seamstresses. At once. (*As* HENRIETTA *moves to the bedroom door* MICHAEL *runs lightly ahead of her, opens it, bowing. All but* CELESTINA *gasp.*) Henrietta, what foolish prank is that?

HENRIETTA. I didn't do anything.

CELESTINA. So, it's Mistress Innocence, is it? Well, bring the pins. What are you waiting for? At once!

HENRIETTA. Yes, Celestina. (*Runs off as others wait with bated breath, returns almost immediately with a large pincushion. All watch as she closes the door carefully and uneventfully. They relax with little movements and murmurs. As* HENRIETTA *starts toward* CELESTINA, MICHAEL *takes the pincushion, lifts it high in the air as he swiftly crosses to* CELESTINA, *bringing it down into her hands.* CELESTINA, *startled, catches it, as though it were a ball unexpectedly thrown.*)

CELESTINA. Henrietta, you threw this at me! How dared you!

HENRIETTA. Oh, no, Celestina, I didn't.

OTHERS. Oh, no. No.

LINA. Truly, she didn't.

LORETTA. It floated through the air. It's magic.

CELESTINA. Stop this babbling of magic. It's nothing but childish tricks. I'll trust none of you until you come to your senses. I must pin up this ruffle myself.

LIZABETTA. Oh, Celestina, I'll do it for you.

PAULINA. Please, let me do it.

CELESTINA. No, you heard me say I will trust no one. Ernestina, you may bring me a stool. (ERNESTINA *brings a stool from one of the dressing tables.* CELESTINA *waves them all away, elaborately seats and settles herself, looks about and chooses* MARIETTA.) Marietta, you may hold the pins. (MARIETTA *takes the cushion, standing on opposite side from where* CELESTINA *will bend over to pin the ruffle and far enough away to make a little ceremony of holding out the cushion each time* CELESTINA *wants a pin.*) There, now I am ready. (MICHAEL *slips behind* CELESTINA.) A pin. (*Takes one from cushion but just before she puts it in ruffle* MICHAEL *carefully takes it from her fingers.*) Oh, I dropped it. Another one. (*This business is repeated twice more,* CELESTINA's *agitation increasing.*)

LORETTA. She's not dropping those pins!

PAULINA. They just disappear.

HENRIETTA. It's magic.

OTHERS (*ad lib.*). Yes. Of course. It's magic.

CELESTINA (*jumps up, furious*). Stop talking about magic! I never heard such nonsense in my life! What a lot of whimpering little nanny goats you are. I tell you it's a trick. It isn't magic! Is isn't magic! (*Her anger has fear in it.*) I won't have any magic here except . . . (*Stops abruptly.*)

LINA. Go on, Celestina. You were going to say that you wouldn't have any magic here except your own. You don't like any magic that you can't control, do you, Celestina? I think maybe you are a little bit frightened, too.

CELESTINA (*glad to escape this by lashing out at* LINA). Well, look who's talking now! I should think you'd said and done enough for one day, Your Royal Highness. Are you looking for another lesson in how a princess should behave?

FLORENTINA. What's she been doing, Celestina?

CELESTINA. Do you know what I found our little princess doing this morning? Accepting a proposal of marriage from the dirty little gardener's boy, ready to run off with him.

SEVERAL. Run away with the gardener's boy!

OTHERS. Marry the gardener's boy!

ALL. How dreadful!

LORETTA. You wouldn't really do it, would you, Lina?

ERNESTINA. You wouldn't really marry the gardener's boy? Oh, what a joke.

MARIETTA. Of course, she wouldn't *really*, Ernestina. She was only flirting with him a little.

PAULINA. And the poor creature took it seriously.

LIZABETTA. Marry a gardener's boy. (*Giggling.*) How silly!

CELESTINA. Oh, she really was going to, make no mistake about it. She meant every word of it.

FLORENTINA. Where were you going to live, Lina? In that dirty little house at the bottom of the garden?

ERNESTINA. Tucked in among the tools, I suppose.

LINA. I'm not going to live in the tool shed. . . .

FLORENTINA. Maybe the gardener's boy wants to live in the palace.

MARIETTA. Maybe he's tired of the tool shed.

PAULINA. Maybe that's why he wants to marry Lina.

LIZABETTA. And she thinks it's because she's so pretty!

LINA. That's not the reason.

MARIETTA. Well, gardening is charming work, I'm sure you'd love it.

FLORENTINA. Carrying water from the well.

PAULINA. Grubbing in the dirt all day.

ERNESTINA. Imagine how your hands would look.

LORETTA. You'd wear one homespun dress all year long. . . .

LIZABETTA. And all those scratchy cotton petticoats. (*Giggles.*)

CELESTINA. Remember, dresses don't matter to Lina. She's the one who never wants another ball dress as long as she lives.

FLORENTINA. Maybe the gardener's boy won't want her when he finds out she can't cook.

MARIETTA. And that she never weeded a garden.

LORETTA. Or scrubbed a floor.

ERNESTINA. Maybe he'll teach her. (*Mimicking.*) Now, dear, this is Lesson Three—Scrubbing a Floor. First, you take this smelly scrubbing brush. . . .

LINA (*almost in tears*). Oh, stop, stop, stop. He's not going to teach me to scrub. . . . (*They all laugh but* HENREITTA, *who runs to* LINA *and puts her arms around her.*)

HENRIETTA. I think you're all cruel to Lina. You're making her cry, and you ought to be ashamed of yourselves. Of course, she's not going to marry the gardener's boy. She was just being kind to him, weren't you, Lina?

LINA. Oh, no, I wasn't. I meant it when I said it. But now I know I'll never do it. I couldn't draw water from the well . . . or tend a garden . . . or live anywhere but in the palace. I'm not strong enough or brave enough. (*Crying.*) I'll never marry the gardener's boy!

CELESTINA. And what's more, you'll never have the chance again.

LINA. What do you mean?

CELESTINA. He's gone. He left, of course.

LINA. I don't believe it.

CELESTINA. What did you think he'd do when he was discovered?

LINA. He'll come back. I know he will.

CELESTINA. If he dares to show his face here again, I'll tell Father every bit of his treachery. Oh, no, he won't come back. He's gone adventuring to another kingdom. Why don't you run after him? I won't stop you. See. (*Puts hand with ring behind back.*) Go crying up and down the highroads for him. . . . (LINA *runs sobbing to the bedroom.*)

MARIETTA (*after a pause*). Well, what an extraordinary way to behave! We were only teasing her.

FLORENTINA. And what a curious thing to say, "I'm not strong enough or brave enough."

CELESTINA. I think you'll find our little Lina won't trouble us this way much longer.

LORETTA. Oh, what do you mean, Celestina? You sound as if you knew a secret. Do you?

MARIETTA. Oh, of course she doesn't, Loretta.

CELESTINA. But, of course I do! The time is coming, and soon, when the ninth prince will ask the hand of one of us in marriage. The ninth prince will take his vigil outside our door, as all the others have done. When we have led him away, as we have led all the others—when he has failed to return and reveal the secret, as all the others have

failed, then there will be a partner for each of us . . .
and we can dance forever.

LORETTA, PAULINA, LIZABETTA. Forever!

MARIETTA, FLORENTINA, ERNESTINA. We will dance forever!

CELESTINA. Never again will Lina rebel. When one more
prince has come . . .

PAULINA (*almost afraid to interrupt*). But, Celestina, it may
not be a prince who comes. Father said he'd let anyone try
to discover the secret of the worn-out shoes.

FLORENTINA. Yes, and he might be a cobbler.

MARIETTA. Or a farmer.

LIZABETTA. Or a blacksmith.

CELESTINA. And he might be a peasant. What difference does
it make? The man will be Lina's partner. Anyone is good
enough for her.

ERNESTINA. Anyone is good enough for Lina.

MARIETTA. We won't have to share our partners with Lina
any more.

CELESTINA. There will be a partner for each of us . . . and
then the spell is sealed forever.

LORETTA (*shivering*). It's so mysterious. How do you know,
Celestina? Who told you?

CELESTINA. I'll have none of your questions, Loretta. Why
are you standing here gabbling? Off with you, all of you,
this instant. There are ball gowns to be fitted, and new
shoes to be chosen.

ALL (*meekly*). Yes, Celestina. (*All go quickly into bedroom,
followed by* CELESTINA. MICHAEL *slumps down dejectedly.
The spirit of the* CHERRY LAUREL *emerges and moves to
comfort him.*)

MICHAEL. Thank you, Cherry Laurel, for your gift of invisibility. I know it will help me to follow the princesses, unseen. I can find out exactly where they go—and the secret of their worn-out shoes. But what good will it do? I can never go to the king and offer to find out the secret. I would never have the chance to try. The minute the Princess Celestina saw me, she would tell her father and have me banished or killed. I see no way to save the Princess Lina.

CHERRY LAUREL. Have you forgotten, Michael, that my sister also has the power to help you?

MICHAEL. The rose laurel! (Goes to ROSE LAUREL.) Shall I pluck this beautiful pink flower from your branches?

ROSE LAUREL. Yes, Michael. (MICHAEL picks flower.) This flower I will make the gift of disguise. Tomorrow night wear it in your buttonhole and you will be disguised as a prince. The Princess Celestina will never guess you are the gardener's boy.

MICHAEL. Oh, thank you, Rose Laurel!

ROSE LAUREL. You have tended us well, Michael.

CHERRY LAUREL. And we have given you our gifts . . . the power of invisibility . . .

ROSE LAUREL. . . . and the power of disguise . . .

BOTH LAURELS. . . . to discover the secret of the worn-out shoes. (Spirits of the LAURELS disappear.)

MICHAEL. Thank you, Lady of the Stars, for the beautiful laurels, and the help of their gifts. (Remembering.) But I have failed in the most difficult task of all. (Bedroom door opens slowly. Laughter and talk are heard. LINA comes in quietly, watching that she is not seen by her sisters, closes door softly.)

LINA (backing away from door, speaks defiantly). I will run

away. I will find him. I will! (MICHAEL *is overjoyed as* LINA *runs to corridor door, flings it open. She falters, stops and then slowly closes it, sinks down, crying.*) I'm afraid. I'm afraid.

CURTAIN

ACT THREE, Scene One

SCENE: *The dressing room late the next night.*

Music is heard at the rise of the curtain. The PRINCESSES, *in ball dresses, over which they wear dressing gowns, have their backs to audience. They turn one at a time, each with a piece of primping business, and begin*

Dressing Table Ballet

which ends with—

ALL. Oh, dear! I shall never be ready for the ball!

MARIETTA. My hair won't curl.

FLORENTINA. My nose is shiny. (*Sits, looks in mirror.*)

LIZABETTA. My dress doesn't fit right.

ERNESTINA. My cheeks aren't pink enough. (*Sits, looks in mirror.*)

CELESTINA. Be quiet! You girls twitter like magpies.

HENRIETTA. You always speak so sharply to us. (*Sits, looks in mirror.*)

PAULINA. My fingernail would break.

LORETTA. My feet hurt so! (*Sits.*)

CELESTINA. It's almost midnight! Hurry, or we shall be late for the ball.

LINA (*fixing her shoe*). Thank goodness! At least, we're all alone tonight.

FLORENTINA. Mercy, what a queer thing to say! Whatever do you mean?

LINA. I was so uneasy last night. I had the queerest feeling— I was sure there was someone in the room with us—just the way it was yesterday morning.

ERNESTINA. Yesterday morning *was* strange. But nothing happened last night.

LINA. Twice I thought I felt someone brush past me. And there was a breath on my mirror, as if someone were standing just behind me, looking over my shoulder. (*A shudder of fear goes over several of them. Ones who are back-to swing around, all look at one another out of the corners of their eyes and draw in their breath.*)

MARIETTA. Oh, how silly! You girls are frightening yourselves half to death. I never heard such nonsense.

LINA. It is not. And I'm not just scaring myself about last night. When we went down the steps to the enchanted woods, someone stepped on the edge of my skirt and I almost fell. It wasn't any of you because I was the last one down.

CELESTINA. You caught it on a nail. You're always so careless.

HENRIETTA. I don't think she's silly. I just remembered something, too. When we were going through the diamond wood I heard a noise, as if someone were breaking off a branch. It made a sharp crack in the stillness. (*Several gasp.*)

FLORENTINA. Oh, you're as addlepated as Lina. It was only an owl screeching in the castle turret.

CELESTINA. Gabble, gabble, gabble. . . . You're always talking. We shall be late for the ball. Are you ready?

ALL (*standing and folding hands*). Yes, Celestina.

PAULINA. No, Celestina.

CELESTINA. And what's the matter now?

PAULINA. We haven't any bouquets.

LORETTA. I wish the gardener's boy were back. I missed my flowers today.

CELESTINA. That's enough from you, Loretta.

HENRIETTA. Couldn't we carry our old bouquets? They were lovely yesterday.

CELESTINA. Let's see. (ALL *pick up bouquets from dressing tables and examine them with backs to audience. When* LINA *picks hers up, she cries out softly, moves D away from others,* HENRIETTA *following her.*)

HENRIETTA. What's the matter, Lina?

LINA. Look what I found in my bouquet! (*Shows small glittering twig.*)

HENRIETTA. What is it? It looks like something I've seen before, but I can't remember where.

FLORENTINA (*comparing bouquets*). What do you think?

MARIETTA, LIZABETTA. Oh, no.

LINA. It's a branch from the diamond wood!

HENRIETTA. That's it! But it wasn't there yesterday.

LINA. Someone hid it there last night. You see, I was right, there was someone with us.

LIZABETTA, ERNESTINA. Far too faded.

MARIETTA. Shall we throw them away?

CELESTINA. Yes, throw them away.

HENRIETTA. But who would think to put it in your flowers? The gardener's boy makes up the bouquets— Lina! The garde . . .

CELESTINA (*having thrown her bouquet on floor, turns*). What are you two whispering about in the corner? Don't you know you'll make us late for the ball? (LINA *can hardly conceal her joy.*) What's the matter?

HENRIETTA. Nothing, Celestina.

CELESTINA. Well—now, is everyone ready?

ALL (*coming into line with folded hands*). Yes, Celestina.

KING (*off*). Girls! (*As each* PRINCESS's *name is called, she turns her head to look at next in line.*) Lina, Loretta, Paulina, Henrietta, Ernestina, Lizabetta, Florentina, Marietta, Celestina!

ALL (*nod*). It's Father. Yes, Father?

KING (*off*). May I come in?

PRINCESSES. Yes, Father. (MARIETTA *opens door. The* KING *strides in, followed by* MICHAEL, *dressed as a prince.*)

KING. Evening, girls.

PRINCESSES. Evening, Father. (KING *comes C,* PRINCESSES *in V formation, with him as apex.* MICHAEL *is DR.*)

KING. Here's another foolish young man who's come to risk his life trying to discover how you wear out your shoes every night. Daughters, this is young Prince . . . um . . . er . . . er . . . (*To* PRINCESSES *on his right.*) Can't remember his name!

PRINCESSES (*on* KING's *right*). Father doesn't know his name!

KING. Well, anyway, a young prince. From the far-away country of . . . (*To* PRINCESSES *on his left.*) Can't remember his country!

PRINCESSES (*on* KING's *left*). Father doesn't know his country.

KING. Well, anyway, a far-away country. A young prince from a far-away country.

PRINCESSES. A young prince from a far-away country.

KING. Come here, young man, come here. Allow me to introduce my daughters. Young man, these are the Princesses (*each curtsies as her name is called*) Celestina, Marietta, Florentina, Lizabetta, Ernestina, Henrietta, Paulina, Loretta, and Lina. Well, young man, I hope I'll

be seeing more of you, but I doubt it—I doubt it. That's
the way it was with all the others—dropped right out of
sight before I'd got used to the look of their faces. Well
. . . I guess we've done our business. Good night, girls.

PRINCESSES. Good night, Father. (KING *goes out door, then
pokes his head back in.*)

KING. Well! Aren't you going to come along and kiss me
good night?

PRINCESSES (*ad lib.*). Yes, Father. Of course, Father. (ALL *run
off, except* LINA, *who stands staring at* MICHAEL.)

LINA. Michael! It *is* you! I thought I must be dreaming when
you walked in the door. Oh, Michael, I thought I should
never see you again!

MICHAEL. Did you think your sister Celestina could really
drive me away, little Princess? She banished me, but I
have hardly left your side since then. I was with you every
moment last night in the enchanted ballroom.

LINA. O-o-oh, then it *was* you! Then the branch in my bouquet—

MICHAEL. Was my message to you, to tell you not to be
afraid—

LINA. It did make me feel happy—but now, I am more afraid
than ever. Michael, what if my sister recognizes you now?
Surely she will, when it was only yesterday that you made
her so angry.

MICHAEL. Neither she, nor any of your sisters, would ever
think a gardener's boy could be a prince.

LINA. But something dreadful will surely happen to you if
you go down to the enchanted ballroom with us. Do not
watch outside the door tonight. . . .

MICHAEL. There is nothing to fear, Princess. Remember that

I went with you last night and saw all your dances and everything that happens.

LINA. But it will be different tonight when you come as a prince trying to find out the secret. There will be a terrible spell to enchant you and you will never see the sunlight of the world again.

MICHAEL. What is the spell?

LINA. I can't remember. But I know it will begin as soon as we reach the ballroom. No prince has returned and you will not be able to fight it—not even you, Michael. Michael, save your life before it is too late!

MICHAEL. If I cannot save you from the enchantment, Princess—if I cannot teach you to live bravely and dance freely as people do in the sunlight—then I will become part of the enchantment, and will be your partner forever—in the shadows.

LINA. No, Michael, you mustn't—

KING (off). Lina! Where's Lina? (Striding into room.) Isn't Lina going to kiss me good night?

LINA. Oh, yes, Father, of course. (Runs and puts arms around him, kisses him.)

KING (patting her). Well, there, that's better. (Releases her as PRINCESSES enter.) Now, then, good night, again. (Kisses each.) Celestina, Marietta, Florentina, Lizabetta, Ernestina, Henrietta, Paulina, Loretta. That's it. (Goes to door, turns.) Where's my young man? I've lost my young man.

PRINCESSES (indicating MICHAEL). Here, Father.

KING. Sorry I can't offer you a bed, young man, but it seems to be part of the bargain that you have to sit up all night, outside the door. Sorry for you, but then think of the reward you'll get if you find out anything. Not that I think you will. (*Speech has carried* KING *and* MICHAEL *off.* PRINCESSSES, *now in a straight line, assume listening poses.*)

CELESTINA. Sh!

MARIETTA. He's locking the door!

FLORENTINA. Sh!

LIZABETTA. The first lock!

ERNESTINA. Sh!

HENRIETTA. The second lock!

PAULINA. Sh!

LORETTA. The third lock!

LINA. Sh!

CELESTINA. It's almost time for the clock to strike midnight. Are you ready?

ALL. Yes, Celestina.

CELESTINA (*triumphantly*). Now, to call the Prince!

LINA. Oh, don't let's bother with him, Celestina. Let's—let's leave him behind. Let's go by ourselves tonight.

CELESTINA. What are you thinking of, Lina? Of course he must go!

FLORENTINA. And it's very nice for you, Lina, that it was a prince who came, after all.

LINA. But I hate to have him disappear the way the rest of them did.

CELESTINA. Stupid girl! Don't you remember, it is the ninth prince who will seal the enchantment—forever!

LINA. Forever? But I didn't know. . . .

MARIETTA. He will seal the enchantment forever.

LIZABETTA, ERNESTINA, HENRIETTA. Forever!

FLORENTINA. He will be Lina's partner—forever.

LINA. No! No!

HENRIETTA, PAULINA, LORETTA. We will never stop dancing!

LINA. But, Celestina . . .

CELESTINA. Call the Prince!

FLORENTINA (going to door). Prince from a far-away country, unlock the door.

MICHAEL (off). Yes, Princess. (Business of locking the door may be repeated in reverse. Door swings open.)

MARIETTA. Enter, Prince from a far-away country. (MICHAEL enters.)

CELESTINA. Prince from a far-away country, will you come with us to the enchanted castle?

MICHAEL. Yes, Princess, I wish to go.

LINA (suddenly running to MICHAEL). No, go away! Don't come, don't come! Save yourself while there is still time!

CELESTINA (crossing swiftly to her, turning ring as she speaks). But there is no time now, little sister. (PRINCESSES go into trance, LINA drifting back to her place.) Listen! (Turns ring second time as clock begins to strike twelve. On first stroke, PRINCESSES pirouette; on second, undo right sleeves of gown; on third, left sleeves; on fourth, fifth and sixth, the front fastenings; on seventh, remove dressing gowns; on eighth, lay them on dressing table stools; on ninth, back in line; on tenth, up on toes and fluff skirts; on eleventh, turn left; on twelfth start walking left. As the twelfth stroke sounds, CELESTINA turns ring the third time, and a trapdoor L slowly rises as

THE CURTAIN FALLS

ACT THREE, Scene Two

SCENE: The enchanted castle. It is the moment of the end of the previous scene.

When the curtain rises eight PRINCES are frozen in atti-

*tudes of the pavane. The clock strikes twelve. On the sixth
stroke the* PRINCES *begin to move.*

1ST PRINCE. The clock is striking midnight. (*Sixth stroke.*)

2ND PRINCE. It is time for us to wake again. (*Seventh stroke.*)

3RD PRINCE. All day we are frozen. (*Eighth stroke.*)

4TH PRINCE. Remembering nothing. (*Ninth stroke.*)

5TH PRINCE. Now we will come to life and dance all night.
(*Tenth stroke.*)

6TH PRINCE. 'Til the cock crows three times. (*Eleventh
stroke.*)

7TH PRINCE. 'Til the princesses' slippers are worn out.
(*Twelfth stroke.*)

8TH PRINCE. What power chains our feet by day and makes
them dance by night?

1ST PRINCE. I can remember now! It is the magic potion!

ALL. From the golden goblet!

1ST PRINCE. The magic potion which cast the spell that froze
our hearts.

ALL. Sh!

1ST PRINCE. The princesses are coming.

2ND, 3RD PRINCES. Down, down, down the hundred steps.

4TH PRINCE. I hear voices in the silver wood.

5TH PRINCE. I remember. The trees are powdered with drops
of silver . . .

6TH PRINCE. Liquid and sparkling in the light of the moon.

7TH, 8TH PRINCES. The princesses are coming.

1ST PRINCE. I hear their laughter in the golden wood.

2ND PRINCE. I remember. The trees glow like giant golden
candles in the night.

3RD PRINCE. They are coming through the diamond
wood . . .

4TH PRINCE. Where every tiny stem sparkles with a hundred diamonds.

5TH, 6TH, 7TH PRINCES. The princesses are coming.

5TH PRINCE. I can see them on the enchanted lake . . .

6TH PRINCE. In the boats, with lanterns shining on the black water.

7TH PRINCE. Listen! I hear another voice among them.

8TH PRINCE. Look! I see a dark figure among the gleaming dresses.

1ST PRINCE. It is another prince come to guess the secret of the worn-out shoes. (*Music begins.*)

1ST, 2ND, 3RD, 4TH PRINCES. The princesses are here.

ALL. We must dance. (PRINCESSES *enter with* MICHAEL. PRINCES *join them in a*

Pavane

MICHAEL *dancing with* LINA. *When the first figure of the dance is completed,* MICHAEL *and* LINA *stop C, looking at each other. Music fades, lights dim on other couples as they continue to perform the pavane.*)

LINA. You can dance as the rest of us do, Michael.

MICHAEL. Yes, Princess.

LINA. But it makes me sad. (MICHAEL *does not answer.*) Michael, if the spell is broken, will you ask for my hand?

MICHAEL. No, for I am a gardener's boy and you are a princess. I will never claim your hand unless you want to come with me freely, whether I am a prince or a gardener's boy, or a shepherd on the mountainside.

LINA. Oh, Michael, I wanted to run away to the mountains with you, but I am not strong enough. I tried—as hard as I could. I tried to keep Celestina from bringing you here. Oh, Michael, I'm not brave enough to save either of us.

MICHAEL. I cannot save you alone, Princess. I have done everything my Lady of the Stars told me to do. But only you can break the spell of the fear in your own heart.

LINA. My sister is beginning to turn the ring now, and soon we will start the dance of enchantment. Save yourself before it is too late, Michael! Leave me here in the shadows, and save yourself!

MICHAEL. I shall try once more, Princess. If we fail, we shall both be sealed in the spell forever, to dance forever— (*Stops as music fades out.* PRINCESSES *glide away from their partners to edge of stage.* PRINCES *come toward* MICHAEL, *speaking with urgency and dread.*)

1ST PRINCE. The enchantment is beginning—

2ND, 7TH PRINCES. The enchantment is strong!

8TH PRINCE. The princesses will weave the enchantment with their dancing.

1ST PRINCE. We who were betrayed by the enchantment speak to you now.

ALL PRINCES. —speak to you now—

3RD, 6TH PRINCES. Betrayed by the golden goblet.

4TH, 5TH PRINCES. We are warning you.

8TH PRINCE. Do not drink the potion from the golden goblet.

ALL PRINCES. Beware of the golden goblet! (MICHAEL *stands C, smiling at their warnings, as the*

Enchantment Dance of the PRINCESSES

begins. PRINCES *fade back and virtually disappear.* PRINCESSES *dance, with* MICHAEL *as focus, the whole being directed toward drawing him in. Singly, or in groups, they attempt it but he resists until* LINA *drifts toward him and holds out her hand. Then he moves to C with her and they dance together, the other* PRINCESSES *continuing to* dance as a background to their duet. At the conclusion of this music and dance, LINA and MICHAEL retain pose, looking at each other. CELESTINA, in silence, takes the cup from MARIETTA and FLORENTINA DR and moves commandingly toward them. LINA, C, does not see her but when the cup comes in MICHAEL's line of vision, he springs from pose and with a strong free movement begins a reprise of Act Two solo with the same music. LINA is alternately drawn by the two strong forces, Michael's gradually becoming the stronger. CELESTINA fades back to R. LINA finally joins MICHAEL and dances freely and beautifully with him. As soon as she does, CELESTINA hands the cup back to MARIETTA and FLORENTINA DR and advances vindictively toward the dancers. As they finish she suddenly steps between them, holding high her hands, and turns the ring.)

CELESTINA. I am turning the ring, little sister— (LINA's gaiety goes out of her and she begins to crumple as she has done before.)

LINA. Michael!

CELESTINA. I am turning the magic ring, little sister— (In the familiar hypnotic trance, LINA moves to MARIETTA and FLORENTINA, takes cup and starts toward MICHAEL.) Prince from a far-away country! The enchanted castle holds no mystery for you now. You have discovered the secret of the worn-out shoes. Drink to your triumph!

MICHAEL (looking at LINA). I will drink the potion from the golden goblet. I will drain the cup, and I will dance with you in the enchanted castle forever! (He raises his hands to the cup and they close on LINA's. At the touch she shudders and cries out.)

LINA. No! Don't drink! (Snatching the cup away.) You have taught me to dance like a free person and I will never dance the dance of enchantment again! (*Facing* CELES-TINA.) I am not afraid of the magic ring. I am not afraid of anything now! (*She has swung back to* MICHAEL, *his hands close again on the goblet and together they dash it to the ground. There is a flashing of lights and immediately the stage begins to grow brighter.*)

PRINCESSES. She has broken the golden goblet!

PRINCES. He has spilled the magic potion!

MARIETTA. The silver wood is gone!

FLORENTINA. The golden wood is gone!

LIZABETTA. The diamond wood is gone!

LORETTA. All the fairy country has crumbled and disappeared!

PRINCESSES. The spell is broken!

PRINCES. The enchantment is over!

LINA, MICHAEL. The spell is broken!

CELESTINA (*raging*). No, no, no! I won't have it! The spell can't be broken! (*Raises ring high, turns it.*)

LIZABETTA. Nothing happens. (*Giggles.* CELESTINA *turns ring second time.* LORETTA *and* ERNESTINA *begin to laugh.*)

PAULINA. Nothing happens. (*Others join in laughter.*)

CELESTINA (*turning ring third time*). When the ninth man comes, my power—

HENRIETTA. But he did come—

LINA. And the spell is broken. (*Laughter from* PRINCESSES.)

CELESTINA. Cursed gypsy, with her promises . . . hateful, cursed ring! (*She hurls it to ground.* ALL *watch silently as she stalks to corner.*)

KING (*off*). Well! Well! This is a surprise!

PRINCESSES (*ad lib.*). It's Father! Father is coming.

PRINCES (*ad lib.*). That's the king. It's the king's voice.

KING (*entering*). Well, well, well, this is a surprise! I looked out of the palace window, and imagine . . . I saw a castle right in the palace garden! But now it's gone and here you are!

PRINCESSES. Imagine! The enchanted castle right in the palace garden!

KING (*to* MICHAEL). Well, young man, it looks as if you had discovered the secret of the worn-out shoes. You know what your reward is. Make your choice.

LINA. Father, he isn't a prince from a far-away country at all. He's really a shepherd boy, and I'm going to marry him and live in the mountains.

KING. What's this? What's this?

LINA. Remember your proclamation, Father—any young man—

KING. Hum . . . yes . . . Astonishing! And a lucky thing, too. Isn't that right, girls?

PRINCESSES. Yes, Father. (PRINCES *step forward.*)

KING. You look very familiar. Oh, yes . . . I remember. You're the other young men who tried to discover the secret of the worn-out shoes, and failed so miserably.

PRINCES. Yes, Your Majesty.

KING. In spite of your failure, you look all right. You can each have one of my daughters. . . . Might as well have nine weddings as one . . . ho . . . ho . . . ho. . . .

PRINCES. Thank you, Your Majesty.

KING. Well, pair off, pair off. There, I guess everybody will live happily ever after. This calls for some kind of celebration. Come on, let's dance 'til we wear our shoes through!

LINA. Oh, Father, let me show you how Michael has taught me to dance . . . it's the best dancing in the world!

(MICHAEL and LINA lead off, other couples joining in one by one. Last of all, the 1ST PRINCE approaches CELESTINA, bows, she reluctantly accepts, gradually responds to the mood, until all are whirling blissfully as

THE CURTAIN FALLS

PRODUCTION NOTES

SETTINGS The bench around the fountain or well can be constructed as three sides of a square if a rounded piece is too difficult to build.

The dressing tables may be painted on the back wall or screens of the set. If curtains are used, each dressing table can be a braced two-dimensional cut-out with separate stools or with stools hinged to the units. For more realistic treatment, three-dimensional tables may be used.

The laurels may be two-dimensional painted cut-outs. If real trees or shrubs are used, they should have a formal, decorative appearance. As the laurels must be placed near jogs or entrances of some kind, the appearance of the blossoms can be manipulated from backstage. They could be made with leaves on one side and flower on the other, attached to a stick which is rotated to make the flower appear. It must be attached in such a way that MICHAEL has no difficulty in removing the flower from the rod.

The enchanted castle ballroom can be suggested with as few as two columns and formal shrubs, either two- or three-dimensional. The painting of the scenery should have both cool and warm colors, the cool picked up by the cool light in the first of the scene and the warm by the bright light at the end of the scene.

HAND PROPERTIES

ACT ONE

Nine water jars	LITTLE GIRLS
Bunch of flowers	MICHAEL
Ring	CELESTINA
Trumpet with banner	HERALD
Scroll, seal and ribbons	"
Silver basket	LADY OF THE STARS
Two laurels	" " " "
Small silver rake	" " " "
Small gold watering-pot	" " " "
Silk towel	" " " "
Wand	" " " "

ACT TWO

Garden basket	MICHAEL
Nine small formal bouquets	"
Magic garden tools	"
White flower	CHERRY LAUREL
Pink flower	ROSE LAUREL
Pincushion (with corsage size pins)	HENRIETTA

ACT THREE
Scene One

Same nine bouquets	On dressing tables
Sparkling twig	LINA's bouquet

Scene Two

Large gold goblet	On stage

COSTUMES

MICHAEL in Act One wears a traditional middle European peasant mountain costume with hat. In Act Two he wears a loose, full-sleeved shirt and close-fitting knee breeches. For Act Three he has an elegant eighteenth-century costume with wig.

The NINE LITTLE GIRLS wear traditional middle European peasant costumes, over stiff petticoats, with variety in color and detail.

The LADY OF THE STARS may have a soft flowing costume in misty blue and grays, with glistening stars in the folds.

The OLD GYPSY WOMAN should be dressed in dark, heavy clothes with a neutral scarf for her head, definitely in contrast to the bright costumes of the GYPSY DANCERS.

The HERALD wears traditional medieval tabard and long hose.

The KING should have an eighteenth-century costume in warm dark colors and wear a crown.

The spirits of the LAURELS should create the impression of dryads, perhaps having slim green costumes with headdresses of branches and leaves.

The PRINCES wear dark rich colors in contrast to the PRINCESSES' light costumes and to make them more shadowy figures in the early part of the scene. Some colors may be warm to be picked up by the light change during the scene.

The PRINCESSES can wear, for economy's sake, one basic ballet costume with three-quarter skirt, this costume never fully revealed until the end of Act Three, Scene One. Over this they can wear in Act One eighteenth-century capes, stoles or overdresses. In Act Two and Act Three, Scene One, the costume is covered by a ruffled dressing gown. Small crowns should be worn in Acts One and Three.

MUSIC

Dances

The following music is suggested as indicative of the proper feeling for the various dances. For the beginning of MICHAEL's solo in Act One, the complete dance in Act Two and for MICHAEL's and LINA's free dance in Act Three:—*Torch Dance* from incidental music for *Henry the Eighth*, Edward German. For LINA's solo in Act One and the pavane in Act Three:— *Pavanne for a Dead Princess*, Ravel. For the gypsy dances:— *Gypsy Dance*, P. Sarasate, Op. 20 or *In Romany—Gypsy Idyls*, E. Poldini, Op. 86, no. 1. (Any gay folk tune for the peasant dance.) For the dressing table ballet:—the ballet music from *Rosamunde*, Franz Schubert, or the 4/4 tempo music for ballet from *Faust*, Gounod, or the *Sleeping Beauty*, Tschaikowsky.

Background

Some directors will want to use much more music as background, for example, for the opening scene of Act One (*Naiads at the Spring*, Juon, Op. 18, no. 1 is suggested), for the opening scene of Act Two and as a bridge between Scenes One and Two of Act Three.

The scenes where MICHAEL presents the bouquets and when he is invisible are other spots where background music would be effective.

The OLD GYPSY WOMAN and the LADY OF THE STARS could each make her entrance to an appropriate theme, then faded and held background through at least part of the ensuing scene. The ethereal music for the LADY OF THE STARS would then be used for the awakening of the LAURELS, thus recalling the influence of the Lady. A strain from the GYPSY WOMAN's theme could be used later when CELESTINA turns the ring.

SOUND

Trumpet
Striking of clock

The Utah Trail

A PLAY OF PIONEER ADVENTURE

BY ALBERT O. MITCHELL

EDITORS' NOTE

The Utah Trail is a historical play containing all the excitement associated with the West. It is based on actual happenings, every incident suggested by some event in the early pioneer days of the Utah Territory. Here is a western story with an appeal to the older boys and girls as well as to the younger ones, because it presents a dramatic picture of real life in those times. It calls for vigorous acting in realistic terms and offers scope for dynamic pantomime. The siege scenes particularly challenge the player's imagination and concentration. The play is a good stepping-stone from the informal drama experiences of the preceding age level into the formal production.

Twelve- to fourteen-year-olds gain confidence in their first attempts at formal theatre by working with more experienced actors. There are two or three parts in *The Utah Trail*, particularly those of Mr. and Mrs. Leigh and Wantah, which could be handled more effectively and with more security by the senior high school age. Younger children can take the parts of Mary and Poone-Kaats. These younger ones need not work at all times with the whole cast, and, when in rehearsal, should be directed in the story-playing manner to gain the most natural playing and give the greatest enjoyment to them and to the group. Many benefits are derived from the wise direction of several age levels working together on a project of this kind.

The language of the play as a whole is simple, natural and easily spoken. The use of Indian words is functional and of great interest, adding zest to the playing. The Indians presented are those of the region and speak as Indians in the author's experience have spoken, in monosyllables and bare subject-predicate sentences, ungrammatically, with Indian words thrust in when they are angry or when the white man's words fail them. The use of "Ugh!", a comic book corruption of the Indian's grunt, should be avoided, as well as any other sounds or words that imply ridicule. It is up to the director to create lively interest in the Indians as real people and to stimulate a desire to master the words of a foreign language so that they can be used with full meaning and feeling in the context of the scenes. Convincing and consistent use of the Indian words throughout the play should help to circumvent sterotyped characterization.

No matter how simple a production is planned, the producing group will gain immeasurably from research covering history, the customs of early ranching and pioneer life, the structure and equipment of homes, the mores of the Indian tribes of Utah, and the dress of pioneers and Indians.

There is much in the way of chills and thrills in the play resulting from the conflict between the two Indian tribes into which the white family finds itself drawn. However, the dominant value of *The Utah Trail* lies in the strength and courage demonstrated by the pioneer family in meeting the problems of their time.

THE UTAH TRAIL
A Play of Pioneer Adventure

CHARACTERS

JOHN LEIGH, rancher, about 40

MRS. LEIGH, wife, about 35

JANE LEIGH, daughter, about 18

EMMA LEIGH, daughter, about 14

TOMMY LEIGH, son, about 12

ROBBIN LEIGH, son, about 10

MARY LEIGH, daughter, about 7

JOE SHEPHERD, a cowboy, about 21

NOKONAH, a Pah-Ute squaw, about 35

KUMO, her son, about 12

POONE-KAATS, Kumo's sister, about 5

WAN-TAH, a Utah chieftain, about 30

PIANG-KA, a Utah warrior, about 40

JACOB HAMBLIN, missionary to the Indians, about 45

LYMAN HOWD, a settler, about 40

ROVER, Tommy's dog

PLACE: Utah Territory

TIME: A little after 1850

ACT ONE: The interior of the log cabin home of the John
Leigh family, seven miles from the frontier set-
tlement of Piute
Late afternoon. Fall

ACT TWO: *The same*
Following night

ACT THREE, Scene One: *An open place in the forest*
Same night or early morning
Scene Two: *Again, the log cabin at the Leigh*
ranch
At dawn, the same morning

NOTE ON THE SETTINGS *

The interior of the log cabin can be a very simple, even a skeleton, set with all but bare essentials eliminated. The main practical requirements are good bracing for the outside door and the window units. Although the action in this set is vigorous, the demands on the setting are few. The rattling of the shutters, ramming of the door, hammering nails in the door, etc., can all be handled by off-stage sound, without the set being touched. There are good opportunities for enhancing the atmosphere and mood with lighting.

Only a very shallow set is required for the exterior in the forest. This scene can be played against a curtain or screens. If the stage is deep enough, only the downstage portions of the other set need be struck. Or if the stage has a deep apron, the scene can be played before the front curtain with the rocks set up in darkness, while music is played to cover any noise.

ACT ONE

SCENE: *The main room of the log ranch house of the John Leigh family, seven miles from the frontier colony of Piute,*

---

* Full production notes and a glossary of Indian words will be found at the end of the play.

in Utah Territory, just past the middle of the last century. Afternoon in the fall. In the rear wall, C,* is a large fireplace unit, with stone hearth raised. Andirons, tripod, and large black iron kettle indicate that the Leigh family do their cooking here. On the shelf above are two large candles in rough holders, a couple of bright Mexican vases and a multicolored Mexican basket plate. R of fireplace is a built-in seat, boxlike, the top of which is a door or lid in two sections. This leads to the cellar below. Above it is a small look-out window. L of fireplace is a huge chest, above which is a tall window with heavy shutter. It is open and the sunlight slants through it from R. Balancing this window, between look-out opening and chimney, a large animal skin adorns the wall. Above fireplace is a deer head, beneath which hangs a rifle. Between the chest and the fire is a deep woodbox partly filled. In the corner near it stands a shotgun. In the wall R is the outside door, of heavy timber, braced and battened, with old-fashioned latch and stout bar. It is a Dutch door and can be used totally or in two sections. Now, the bar stands in a jog in the wall, bottom section is shut, the top open, and the afternoon sun pours in through the opening. Upstage of this is a high, old-fashioned cupboard with a calendar on it. When the curtained top doors open, colored dishes can be seen on the shelves. In the wall DL, a door leads into another room. Upstage of that is a water barrel, over which hangs a dipper, and a big flour bin. Above the barrel hangs a bright Navajo rug, and above the bin is a shelf, and under that a rack with polished cow horns used as hooks for a sunbonnet, a sombrero, a leather coat with fringes, and a pistol with holster

* The following abbreviations are used throughout: C—center stage; R—right stage; L—left stage; U—upstage; D—downstage.

and cartridge belt. Various other frontier articles are in evidence. In the center of the room is a rough table with benches pushed under. Table is draped with ample cloth of red and white checks. A rocking chair is near the fireplace.

As the curtain rises, a girl's voice can be heard singing "Oh, Susannah!" JANE, in a pink and white checked dress with dark blue bows is seated on a stool L of table churning. After a moment, she stops, lifts the churn lid and looks inside. She moves the dash around. It is almost done. Replacing the lid, she resumes churning and begins to whistle "The Little Log Cabin in the Lane." Breaking off in a moment, she inspects the butter again. This time, seemingly satisfied and pleased, she pours the buttermilk off into a small open-topped keg and places both in the corner UL.

JANE. Well, at last that's done. (She looks at the sun streaming in, then towards the inner door. Goes through the door L. There is a wild wolf howl from outside, and TOMMY, dressed in plaid shirt and buckskin pants, dashes inside door R, ducks behind it and peers out through open top door. Leveling his toy gun over the bottom section of the door, he emits a sound resembling a barrage. Then, ducking, he runs to the door L, as though he might enter. JANE calls from inside room L.) Tommy? (TOMMY jumps, but does not answer. He runs to flour bin as though to hide behind it; thinks better of it, and runs to cellar door R of fireplace. He lifts the door and, just as the feathered head of an Indian boy appears in the doorway R, blots himself out under the lid. The young Indian, KUMO, looks in cautiously, tiptoes to door L. Afraid to go in, he peers timidly behind flour bin; then he moves to the window UL, looks out, grunts, and darts out door he entered by.

JANE comes back, carrying a sunbonnet, fixing to go out
of doors, as MARY enters from outside.)

MARY (off). Janie! . . . Janie (inside now), where's Mother?

JANE. She's in the field, Mary, with Papa and the boys.

MARY. Is Emma with them?

JANE. Yes, Emma, too.

MARY. And Nokonah Squaw, too?

JANE. Umhum.

MARY (dipping a drink from the barrel). Are they still picking
potatoes?

JANE (tidying her hair). Of course, dear. Why aren't you
helping them?

MARY (drinking). Oh, I've been playing pioneer-and-Indian
with Tommy and Kumo.

JANE (finishing her hair). Why isn't Tommy helping Papa?

MARY (setting lid back on barrel, hanging up dipper). Well,
Kumo is supposed to be helping Nokonah, isn't he?

JANE (untying apron). Then why isn't he? Aren't the Indians
supposed to pick up the small potatoes for themselves?

MARY (crossing R to cupboard). Oh, Kumo is like his pappy—
Pah-Quitch lets his squaw do all the work. (She opens the
cupboard door and reaches in the jar for a cookie.)

JANE (taking off apron). Well, let's go and help the menfolks,
Mary. Father wants to get all the crops in and the sup-
plies hauled to the fort at Piute this week.

MARY (shutting cupboard and munching cookie). And then
will he move us all into the big new fort on Sunday?

JANE. (taking apron into the other room). Umhum. On Sunday. If we all pitch in and help.

MARY. Oh, good! (Jumping.) Let's go out and help with the
work, then. (She starts out.)

JANE (coming back in). Here, honey, hold this mirror.

MARY. Jane, does Nokonah have just two papooses?

JANE (*arranging her bonnet*). Just two papooses.

MARY. Just Kumo and Poone-Kaats?

JANE. Umhum.

MARY. Nokonah is afraid the Utah Indians will steal her papooses. Isn't she?

JANE. Yes, dear.

MARY. Why?

JANE. Because they stole one of them once before.

MARY. They did? Why?

JANE. To sell to the slave traders.

MARY. To the slave traders? Why?

JANE. For slaves. The Utahs can get money by selling Pah-Ute children for slaves.

MARY. Are Kumo and Poone-Kaats Pah-Ute children?

JANE. Yes.

MARY. Why?

JANE (*laughing*). Because their mother and father are Pah-Utes, silly.

MARY (*apprehensive*). Our papa won't let the Utahs steal us, will he?

JANE (*stooping to tie* MARY's *bonnet*). Of course not. (*As* MARY *admires herself in the mirror,* JANE *kisses her playfully.*) Come, honey. Let's go and help Papa get off to the Fort. (*She goes out.*)

MARY (*putting mirror on table hurriedly*). Well, Jane . . . does Nokonah— (*As* MARY *disappears,* TOMMY, *who has been eavesdropping from under the cellar door, lifts the door, steps out and sneaks to the door, R. Just then,* KUMO's *war whoop can be heard. Swiftly,* TOMMY *runs to the window UL, and leaps outside from the chest, just as* KUMO *appears, looking over the bottom door, R.* KUMO

*looks around cautiously. Then, with stealthy step, he enters
and explores the place. Near the table, he spies the mirror,
picks it up and looks at himself. Surprised at his own re-
flection, he starts back. Grunt.* TOMMY, *at window, points
toy gun at* KUMO's *back.*)

TOMMY. I've got you covered, Injun! (KUMO *puts mirror
down hastily.*) Don't move, or I'll send you humping to
the happy hunting ground. (KUMO *wheels abruptly, bow
and arrow ready, but* TOMMY *has gone. With a yelp,* KUMO
is on the chest and out the window. . . . ROBBIN, *in blue
jeans and rough shirt, comes in leading* ROVER.)

ROBBIN (*off*). Tommy! (*Coming in.*) Tommy, Papa wants
you—

TOMMY (*reappearing under cellar door, finger to lips*).
Sh-h-sh! No peshadny!

ROBBIN (*about to look in bedroom, whirls*). Papa wants you—

TOMMY (*pointing to door*). Mah-be-nunk!

ROBBIN. Oh, stop talking Indian!

TOMMY. Look, Robbin—Kumo's after me. He's pretending
to be an enemy Indian—a Utah! Hide in the bedroom.

ROBBIN. But—but Papa—

TOMMY (*jerking thumb L*). Pun-kerro!—scoot! (*Then as* ROB-
BIN *starts to go.*) No, wait! Let's trick him with our owl
signals!

ROBBIN (*entering into the spirit of the game*). You mean
signals—Hoo-oot—like we do with Papa?

TOMMY. Yes—you run through the bedroom, crawl out the
window and come around to this one. (*Points to window,
UL.*)

ROBBIN (*going*). Sure, and then we'll fool him with our owl
signals.

TOMMY. Pssst! Take Rover. You want him to give me away?

(ROBBIN *goes with dog.* TOMMY *ducks under lid as* KUMO *appears at the window. Peering out, he tries to watch* KUMO.) Hoo-oot! (KUMO *jerks and looks inside.*) Hoo-oot! (KUMO *comes inside and looks in fireplace, searching.* ROBBIN *appears at window behind* KUMO.)

ROBBIN. Hoo-oot! (*With a whirling leap,* KUMO *is out the window, but* ROBBIN *has gone.* TOMMY *lifts the lid, laughing softly, takes a cartridge shell from his pocket, blows on it for a whistle. Startled, as* ROBBIN *appears beneath the lid with him, he jumps and exclaims—*)

TOMMY. Robbin!

ROBBIN. Sh-sh-sh!

TOMMY (*chuckling*). Kumo'll never find our secret passage. (*They laugh together.* ROBBIN *takes the whistle and blows it.*)

ROBBIN (*handing whistle back*). I'll bet that's why Papa cut that hole in the shed floor!

TOMMY. Sure, so if Indians ever attacked us—

ROBBIN. We could go down through the cellar (*he indicates*) and up through the shed!

TOMMY. Ha-ha! Kumo, the jack rabbit! (*They laugh again, not realizing that* KUMO *is watching them from chest under window, L. He draws a bead on* TOMMY's *back.* TOMMY, *suddenly seeing him out of the corner of his eye, whirls and pulls* ROBBIN *under the lid with him. Repeating his wolf howl,* KUMO *is coming into the room when* MOTHER *appears in the doorway, R.*)

MOTHER (*advancing*). Here you, Kumo, what's all this wolf howling? Where's Tommy? What are you up to?

KUMO (*starts to climb back out*). Me no Kumo—

MOTHER. What—?

TOMMY (*appearing behind* MOTHER). He's not Kumo—he's

Wah-karrah, the Utah, the Yellow Hawk! That's why he makes the wolf howl.

MOTHER. Goodness, Tommy! Where did you come from?

TOMMY (*folding his arms and speaking gravely, Indianlike*). Mike-tickaboo! The secret way! The tunnel from the cellar (*pointing*) to the shed.

MOTHER (*going to the churn by the water barrel*). Oh, Tommy, will you never grow up? Where's Robbin? We sent him in to get you. (*Carries churn to bench back of table.*)

TOMMY. Robbin? (*Just then* ROBBIN *lifts the cellar lid, stands beside* TOMMY. TOMMY *shrugs—Indian style.*) Umpio. (*He is slyly edging toward the door R, covering* ROBBIN'S *retreat. When* ROBBIN *has leaped out the door behind him—*) Oh, Robbin—? He's gone out to help Pa!

MOTHER (*noticing cellar lid up, catching on*). I see. (*Closing lid, crossing back into room, L.*) Your father needs you, too, Tommy.

TOMMY (*starting out*). I'm going, Mother. (*Sees* KUMO *stealing out window, aims toy gun at him.*) Here, ye skulking jack rabbit! Piek-a! (*He jerks his thumb at* KUMO.)

KUMO. No me jack rabbit! (*Still playing he's the Utah chief.*)

TOMMY. Pa told me Kumo means jack rabbit in Pah-Ute language.

KUMO (*laughing, giving up*). Ummh! Me Kumo. Me Pah-Ute! Tickaboo—tickaboo!

TOMMY (*teasing*). Tickaboo? Huh, you are not a friend. You shot at me. You're enemy!

KUMO. No. Not enemy. (*Seriously.*) Much friend.

TOMMY (*with a big smile, dropping the play*). All right. (*He produces a gold watch from pocket.*) Here, papoose, you want to see something?

KUMO (*eyes bulging*). Um-ummh! Wah-pana-karrah!

TOMMY. Wah-pana—gold? Sure it's gold. My grandfather wore that watch across the plains. (*He holds it to* KUMO'S *ear.*)

KUMO (*charmed*). Hum-pah!

TOMMY (*laughing, delighted*). Hear it tick, Tickaboo?

KUMO (*holding out his hand*). Mug-gi. (*Holds watch to ear.* TOMMY, *fishing in his pockets, brings out cartridge shell, blows on it for whistle.* KUMO *is more surprised.*) Mumpi!

TOMMY. It's a bullet shell. (*He blows it again.*)

KUMO (*reaching for it*). Yenno-yack!

MOTHER (*coming back in*). Now you two clear out. (TOMMY *recovers his things.* KUMO *jumps and starts out window.*) Off with you. Vamoose!

KUMO. Mc go.

MOTHER. Oh, Kumo, Nokonah has gone to the wickiup.

KUMO. Um-ummh! (*He goes. Taking butter mold from cupboard,* MOTHER *moves to table, fills mold from churn and begins to work the butter.*)

TOMMY (*taking a pencil from his pocket*). Why is Kumo's mother going to the wickiup so early? To take his little sister home?

MOTHER. Yes.

TOMMY. Is she afraid the Utahs will get her papoose? (*He writes on calendar which hangs on cupboard.*)

MOTHER. Yes. Don't write on the calendar, Tommy.

TOMMY (*putting pencil back in pocket*). Are they on the warpath?

MOTHER. The Utahs? She thinks they're around and she's going to hide her children.

TOMMY (*near door, R*). Well, when Jacob Hamblin was here last night, didn't he say—

MOTHER. He said they may go on the warpath, and Brigham Young has asked him to go across the river tomorrow and talk with Wah-karrah, the Utah chief.

TOMMY. Well, Joe told him we ought to stop talking and go over there with the militia.

MOTHER. Yes!

TOMMY. Joe says the only good Injun is a dead Injun.

MOTHER. Yes—well, remember the Utahs burned Joe's home that time. He can't help feeling bitter.

TOMMY. Is Papa still going to Piute tonight?

MOTHER. Yes. Now go along and help him get ready.

TOMMY. Could the Utahs get us if we were inside the big mud fort?

MOTHER. It's safer there.

TOMMY (aiming his gun out over the bottom door). If Indians tried to come over those high walls, we could shoot them.

MOTHER. Let's hope we won't need to.

TOMMY (looking out). Oh, here's Papa now, and Joe, too. (Comes closer to MOTHER.) Is Joe going to Piute with him?

MOTHER. Yes.

TOMMY. Why couldn't I go instead?

MOTHER. Papa will need Joe to help with finishing our house in the fort.

FATHER (entering, with a large wooden grub box, and a water bag over one arm). Tommy, aren't you ashamed to let your sisters do the outside work? (He sets box on table.)

TOMMY. Yes, Papa, but—well, couldn't I go to Piute with you instead of Joe?

FATHER (going with water bag to barrel, UL). I need Joe to help me finish the house there.

TOMMY But I could help you. And I could ride my pinto pony and—

FATHER (*dipping himself a drink at the barrel*). You could help Mother right here. She'll need you while I'm gone.

TOMMY (*not too happy*). All right, Papa. (*As he goes,* JOE, *a tall young man dressed in picturesque fashion of the frontier, enters, ruffling* TOMMY's *hair as they pass in the doorway.*)

FATHER. Did you find all the cattle, Joe?

JOE. Um-hum. (*Tips his hat on the back of his head.*)

FATHER. Any signs of wild animals bothering them?

JOE. No—only two-legged wild animals. (*He reaches down his rifle from over the fireplace.*)

FATHER. Indians? (*He looks at* JOE *curiously.*)

JOE. Umhum. Utahs, I'd say.

FATHER. Utahs?

JOE (*nods*). Pony tracks all over the range.

FATHER. Looking the cattle over, you think?

JOE. Reckon so. And we'd better watch Tommy's spotted horse. You know how Indians go for painted ponies.

FATHER. But you found all the cattle?

JOE. Brought them into the inner pasture.

FATHER. Then we needn't worry.

JOE (*with meaning*). Been lots of cattle disappearing up north lately.

FATHER (*passing it off, as he fills water bag with dipper*). Oh, they're probably friendly Indians.

JOE (*working with gun*). Just the same, John, we ought to get the guns in order.

FATHER. Think so, Joe?

JOE. Well, you heard what Jacob Hamblin said last night.

FATHER. Yes, the Utahs are restless.

JOE (*his lips tight*). Restless enough to hit the trail.

FATHER (*going into other room*). Jacob is going to parley with Chief Wah-karrah soon.

JOE. Yeah—well, maybe Jacob can talk the warpaint off the chief, but can Wah-karrah control his Utah braves?

MOTHER (*at table, still working butter*). The Pah-Ute squaw is nervous.

FATHER (*coming back with bedroll which he sets on the floor and lashes*). She's taking her papooses to the mountains.

MOTHER. You can't blame her. She's lost one child to the slavers.

JOE. Thanks to the Utahs!

MOTHER. She seems to feel the Utahs are near now.

JOE (*looking down his sights*). So do I.

FATHER (*shouldering bedroll, starting out*). Well, Joe, come and help me get ready.

JOE. Aren't you going to clean that shotgun?

FATHER. Oh—before I go. I'd like to get off in time to reach the Fort before dark, though. (*He goes.*)

MOTHER (*calling after him*). I'll have your grub box and things ready.

FATHER (*off*). All right. (JOE *hangs his gun over the mantel, goes out.* . . . MOTHER *busies herself with packing the grub box. Her back is to the door, when a shadow suddenly appears on the floor. She wheels abruptly to see* NOKONAH *whisk fearfully inside the door, pushing ahead of her a small Indian girl almost completely wrapped in a blanket.*)

MOTHER. Nokonah!

NOKONAH (*pulling blanket off child and pushing her forward*). Papoose! Poon-e-kee!

MOTHER. What—what do you want?

NOKONAH. Pun-kerro! Utah!

MOTHER. Utah?

NOKONAH (*nodding excitedly, she pushes child forward desperately, then glides back to door, looks out, turns*). You keep? (MOTHER *nods.* NOKONAH *goes, silently as she came.* MOTHER *stands petrified for a second, looking around for possible places to hide* POONE-KAATS. *She sets butter mold on the mantel, then darts to door L, halts on threshold, turns to bin, lifts lid, hesitates, shuts lid; then snatches* POONE-KAATS *by the hand and runs to cellar door. Lifting lid, she tries to put the child under. Terrified,* POONE-KAATS *resists, not understanding.*)

POONE-KAATS. Pe-ats!

MOTHER. No. Nokonah go away.

POONE-KAATS (*cries out*). Nokonah! (*Sensing the presence of Indians,* MOTHER *suddenly snatches* POONE-KAATS *by main force and swings her behind herself just as a feathered head appears in window, L. Without looking at him, she stands rigid and steadily reaches for butter mold she left on mantel. The feather-framed face disappears.* MOTHER *puts her hand on child's head. A long shadow falls across the floor from doorway, R.*)

WAN-TAH (*tall, fierce-looking Utah, appearing in doorway.*) Unnh!

MOTHER. What do you want?

WAN-TAH (*ominously*). Nan-zitch. Wan-tah want papoose!

MOTHER. Go away!

WAN-TAH. White squaw hide papoose. Mug-gi! (*He gestures toward her and back to himself.*)

MOTHER. Vamoose. Squaw not here.

WAN-TAH. Squaw—maybe so. Papoose, you hide. (MOTHER, *striving to keep cool, returns his stare. He hesitates, studying her, then moves to the door, calls over shoulder.*)

Piek-a! (PIANG-KA, *another Utah, appears.* WAN-TAH, *with his eyes, indicates the other is to search.* PIANG-KA *looks at* MOTHER, *then looks toward the bedroom, his eyes suggesting he search it.* WAN-TAH *grunts. The* OTHER *starts in.*)

MOTHER (*bluffing, stalling for time*). No! (PIANG-KA *whirls, faces her.*) In-ne-to-ah! (*The* INDIAN *hesitates.*) You can't go in there! (PIANG-KA *looks to* WAN-TAH. *After a searching pause,* WAN-TAH *nods, almost imperceptibly. The* OTHER *goes in.*) Utah is coward. Mi-poodg-e! He comes while white man is gone.

WAN-TAH (*his head goes up*). To-buck! (PIANG-KA *returns from searching the other room, moves toward* MOTHER, *impassive, yet with a searching eye, looking in every corner. Sees the mirror left on the table, turns slyly, without expression—except a glance at* WAN-TAH—*slips mirror in his pouch, covering so* MOTHER *does not see. Looks stolidly at* WAN-TAH, *who grunts. Then his roving eye lights on the flour bin. He stalks over to it, looks in, but keeps eye on* MOTHER. *Grunt.*)

MOTHER. That's only flour. (*She puts butter mold on shelf again.* WAN-TAH *then comes to the bin. Looks in and grunts surprise and satisfaction.*)

PIANG-KA. Tu-shu-krnt! (*He reaches a handful of flour.*)

WAN-TAH. Prowa! (WAN-TAH *takes flour, then moves back to the door, watching* MOTHER *still. After peering outside, he looks back at* PIANG-KA, *who stealthily filches some matches from the shelf.*)

MOTHER. No. You can't have matches. (PIANG-KA, *watching her, pouches them just the same.* WAN-TAH *turns, looking out again. As he does so* POONE-KAATS *peers out from behind* MOTHER *with frightened eyes.* PIANG-KA *does not see.*

MOTHER *pushes her back swiftly.* WAN-TAH, *seeing only a motion, whirls quickly.*)

WAN-TAH. White squaw hide papoose!

MOTHER (*bluffing*). Wan-tah is cunning. You find papoose.

WAN-TAH (*moving L as* PIANG-KA *counters R to door, and indicating* MOTHER *is to move R*). Meah-bike-way!

MOTHER. No. (WAN-TAH *slides hand to knife, jerks head right.*) No. You go. Pi-queah! White man come soon. (*The* IN-DIANS *exchange glances,* PIANG-KA *looks out cautiously.* WAN-TAH *advances, motions her to move.*)

WAN-TAH. Meah-bike-way! (MOTHER *hesitates, then shifts carefully R.* WAN-TAH, *with quick tread, steps onto the stone hearth to look behind her. She stands steady, staring him in the eye. With quick action, he gets to the door. Watching her and moving head slightly to* PIANG-KA—) Poony—Punkerro! (*While they are at the door,* POONE-KAATS *lifts* MOTHER's *skirts—for she is now under them— and peers out again, frightened.* MOTHER *covers her head in a flash as* PIANG-KA *goes and* WAN-TAH *turns sharply to confront her, fingering his tomahawk.*) Now . . . You tellum Wan-tah. (*Pause.*) At-am-bar!

MOTHER. You find papoose.

WAN-TAH (*advancing darkly*). Me find! (MOTHER *stands her ground.*) Wan-tah want papoose!

MOTHER. To trade to the slavers!

WAN-TAH. So—! You got papoose! (*Gestures her to give.*) Mug-gi!

MOTHER (*shakes her head and holds her ground till he forces her to retreat*). No! (*He lifts his tomahawk.*) No! . . . No!! (*As* WAN-TAH's *weapon is lifted,* FATHER, *who has suddenly appeared in the doorway and taken the situation in at a glance, leaps swiftly across the room. Now, he*

grasps WAN-TAH's *left shoulder with his right hand, spins
him around and deals him a left to the jaw which sends
him reeling to the floor with his head near the inner door.
While this action is taking place,* POONE-KAATS *slips from*
MOTHER's *skirts and gets under the cellar lid.* FATHER
stands over WAN-TAH, *waiting for him to get up.* WAN-TAH
*rises slowly, watching his fallen weapon out of the corner
of his eye. But* FATHER *too is watching, and when* WAN-TAH
leaps for it, FATHER *anticipates him and gets it first.* WAN-
TAH *rises, backing to front of table. As he touches the
corner of it, he suddenly lifts his knife from his belt and
flashes it menacingly. But, again,* FATHER *is ahead of him
and has the tomahawk raised threateningly.*)

FATHER (*gesturing with head toward door*). Now, scoot, you
skunk! (WAN-TAH *watches, defying him.*) Vamoose!

WAN-TAH (*backs to door, looks out*). Wan-tah go. (*More
darkly.*) Wan-tah come back! (*Looks out.*) Piek-a! (*He
vanishes.* FATHER *follows him to door and looks after him,
then—*)

FATHER (*rushing to* MOTHER). Molly—

MOTHER (*looking around, dazed*). Where's the papoose?

FATHER. Papoose—?

MOTHER. The child, Poone-kaats—she was here just now.

FATHER. Here? Where?

MOTHER (*lifting skirts*). Here.

FATHER (*puzzled*). What? (MOTHER *looks toward door.*) She
must have slipped out while he wasn't looking.

MOTHER. Oh! Go quick, John—they'll catch her! (FATHER
hesitates at the door. MOTHER *is looking out window L.*
POONE-KAATS' *head appears under cellar door.* MOTHER *and*
FATHER *see her together.*)

POONE-KAATS. Nokonah! Pe-ats?

MOTHER (*rushing to her*). Of course you want your mother. (*She lifts her out of the box, then turns to* FATHER.) Oh, John, the children! (FATHER *jumps, rushes to the door just as* TOMMY *and* EMMA *come hurrying in.*)

TOMMY (*off*). Papa! Papa!

MOTHER (*as they come in*). Oh, Tommy—Emma! Where's Robbin? Where's my baby?

EMMA. They're coming.

TOMMY. They were in the wagon with Jane and Joe.

ROBBIN (*off*). Hurry. (*Rushing it with* MARY.) Papa, what were those Indians doing in here?

MARY. We saw them sneaking away.

FATHER (*laying tomahawk on shelf, L*). Did they see you?

ROBBIN (*spying tomahawk*). Papa, where did you get that?

TOMMY. Wow! It's a tomahawk! (*They run to inspect it.*)

FATHER (*reaching for the shotgun*). Did the Indians see you, Tommy?

TOMMY. No, we hid behind the load of potatoes.

ROBBIN. Kumo said they were Utahs. (NOKONAH *appears in the doorway. As her child is behind* MOTHER, *the squaw does not at first see her. Her eyes find* MOTHER.)

NOKONAH. Pat-sun?

MOTHER. Nokonah!

NOKONAH. Te-ah—Papoose?

POONE-KAATS (*running to her*). Nokonah! (FATHER *puts down shotgun.*)

NOKONAH (*stooping down to meet her, suddenly straightens, looks around, questioning*). Kumo—?

MOTHER. Kumo? Why—

NOKONAH (*with a wild look toward door*). Katz-karrah! Kumo go?

TOMMY. Kumo went to look for you.

MOTHER. Kumo went to the wickiup. (NOKONAH *lets out a cry. Just then* KUMO *appears in the window as before and playfully gives his wolf cry. The cry is cut short by the hand of* WAN-TAH, *who jerks the boy away and disappears.*)

MOTHER. Wan-tah!

NOKONAH. Utah! (*She dashes for the door.*)

POONE-KAATS (*following*). Utah!

ROBBIN (*at the window*). There's two of them!

TOMMY. They're putting him on a horse! (FATHER *grabs* JOE'S *rifle, aims it out window.*)

MARY. Hurry, Papa. They've got Kumo.

MOTHER. Oh, don't shoot, John. You'll hit the boy! (*As children rush outside—*) Jane— Watch the children!

JANE (*at door*). All right, Mother. (*Goes.*)

JOE (*agitated, as he comes in*). Aren't we going after that son-of-a-savage? (*He goes to* FATHER *who still has* JOE'S *gun.* FATHER *gives it to him.*)

FATHER. No, Joe. No use trying to overtake the thieves. They're moving too fast, and they're desperate.

JOE. And mean!

FATHER. Yes, they're desperate. The big one—what's his name?

MOTHER. Wan-tah.

FATHER. He threatened to come back.

JOE. Then why don't we go after him?

FATHER. We'd never make it. They'd ambush us, Joe.

JOE. Then let's get the militia and wipe them out.

FATHER. Let's think of Kumo. . . . We'll try to trade for the boy.

JOE. Trade for him—with the Utahs!

FATHER. When I get to the Fort tonight, I'll tell Jacob

Hamblin about him. He will talk to Wah-karrah, their chief.

JOE. This Wan-tah is a renegade!

FATHER. But he'll trade with Jacob Hamblin.

JOE (*relaxing*). All right. But we'd better take the family with us to the fort.

FATHER. We planned that the family should stay here to get things ready and to watch the cattle and property while you and I finish the house.

JOE. It's true there's no place for cattle near the Fort just now. The grazing is poor close in.

FATHER. Anyway, the fort isn't quite finished. . . . But if you'd feel better, Molly (*looking at* MOTHER), suppose we leave Joe here with the family.

MOTHER. Do you think the Utahs will bother us, John?

FATHER. No . . . now that they've got Kumo, they have part of what they came for. They know the squaw will hide the other child. They won't be this way again for a while.

MOTHER. You're right, and we must save our cattle and property.

JOE (*hanging up his rifle*). I'll stay here anyway, and lend a hand watching the cattle—and the children. There'll be others who'll help you finish the house.

FATHER. I'll manage. (*Quietly, patting* JOE *on the shoulder.*) I've never carried a grudge against the Indians, but keep your eyes open and your gun cocked, Joe.

MOTHER (*putting the last of food into the grub box*). Will you wait for supper, John, or— I've put some sandwiches on top. (*Indicating box.*) You can eat as you go, then you won't be so late getting there.

FATHER. Well— (*He closes grub box, and reaches coat from the rack, L.*)

MOTHER (*going to door and calling off*). Jane, bring the children in now. Father's ready to go.

JANE (*off*). Yes, Mother. They're all here. (*JOE hangs his pistol under shelf, L, takes pail from behind cupboard and goes out.*)

FATHER (*his coat partly on*). Molly—do you really think I ought to go?

MOTHER. We'll be all right, John.

FATHER. Should I wait until morning and—

MOTHER. And take us with you? (*FATHER nods.*) We're not ready, and the Indians might steal the cattle if we weren't here to watch. Now that Joe's going to stay with us, we'll be all right.

FATHER. All right. (*Takes his hat, as the children come trooping in.*) Now, let's see you all. (*He stands in front of table and they line up in front of him.*) I'll be gone for three nights. I want you all to do as Mother tells you. Do your work well and get things ready.

ROBBIN. Can we live inside the big wall then?

FATHER. Yes, Robbin.

MARY. And go to church on Sunday?

EMMA. But is the mud wall finished?

TOMMY. Jacob Hamblin says it's almost done.

FATHER. I want all of you to promise you won't go out without Jane or Mother till I get back.

TOMMY. Sure.

ROBBIN, MARY. Yes, Papa.

EMMA. Yes, Father.

ROBBIN. Is Joe going to the fort with Papa?

MOTHER. No, dear, Joe's going to stay right here with us.

MARY. Well, then, we can go with Joe to herd the cattle, can't we?

FATHER (*taking her in his arms*). No, little bird, you mustn't go out of this yard. When we move into the fort, you can play all over it—

MARY. Oh, goody! (CHILDREN *all begin to chatter.*)

MOTHER. Hush now, everybody! Father has to get started.

FATHER (*starting to pick up his grub box*). Good-bye, young 'uns. (*They all try to grab it and help* FATHER *out.* EMMA *and* ROBBIN *scuffle, finally carrying it out between them.* MARY, *failing to get hold of the box, contents herself with carrying out the water bag* FATHER *filled. They all go noisily out except* TOMMY, *who lingers by the door and stops* FATHER.)

TOMMY. Will you try to get Kumo, Papa?

FATHER. Yes. I'll tell Jacob Hamblin about him as soon as I get to the fort.

TOMMY. He could trade something to the Utahs for Kumo, couldn't he?

FATHER. Yes, I think he could. . . . Indians like spotted ponies, Tommy.

TOMMY. Well, tell Jacob he can trade my pinto pony—if they won't take anything else.

FATHER (*smiling—understanding*). I will, son. (*He hugs* TOMMY. TOMMY *gulps and goes out.* FATHER *turns to* MOTHER. *They look at each other. She comes to him. He pats her on the shoulder.*)

MOTHER. Don't worry, John. We'll be all right. (FATHER *smiles and goes.*)

CHILDREN (*off, as* MOTHER *stands in doorway*). Good-bye, Papa!

TOMMY. Don't forget about Kumo!

EMMA. Hurry so you'll be inside the walls before dark!

ROBBIN. And get our house finished!

MARY. And bring us all a lump of sugar! (*There is a sound of wagon and horses receding, the dog barks.* MOTHER *waves.*)

CHILDREN (*off*). Good-bye. Good-bye.

FATHER (*faintly*). Good-bye. Good-bye.

MOTHER (*in doorway, calling off*). Now, children, finish your chores and come right inside. Tommy, you feed the pigs and chickens; Emma, you bring in the milk when Joe has finished milking; Robbin, you fetch in the wood, and, Mary, you help Robbin. (*It is growing darker outside.* MOTHER *busies herself with preparations for supper, first getting ready to kindle a fire.* ROBBIN *comes in with wood, bangs it in woodbox. Going back for more, he bumps into* MARY, *who drops her wood on the floor just inside the door.*)

MARY. Oh, Robbin, look where you're going!

ROBBIN. Well, you go where you're lookin'!

MOTHER (*as they face each other somewhat belligerently*). Children!

ROBBIN. All right. (*Goes.* MARY *carries the wood, a piece at a time, to woodbox.* EMMA, *bringing the milk, takes jars from the lower part of the cupboard, pours milk in them, sets them inside lower shelves, closes doors.* ROBBIN *comes in with more wood, then* TOMMY *appears with a bucket, which he sets near the flour bin.*)

MOTHER. Now, each of you take a bucket and go to the spring for water. It's good to have water on hand. . . . (*She breaks off, looking at* ROBBIN, *who has picked up the bucket* TOMMY *has put down.*) Robbin! Not the swill bucket! (ROBBIN *jumps, looks at the bucket; then with a silly gesture, sets it back, L. They all burst out laughing and go swinging out with their buckets.*) Goodness!

MARY (*as she goes*). Robbin thinks we're all pigs! (*She laughs again; the others join her.*)

MOTHER (*anxiously, meeting* JANE *at the door*). Jane, follow them.

JANE (*snatching a shawl from rack*). Br-r-r! It's getting chilly. (*Goes.* MOTHER *looks out window, then lights the fire. The dog barks.* MOTHER *stands, listening as* JOE *comes in.* JOE *stops and looks at her.*)

MOTHER (*significantly*). Wolves, maybe?

JOE (*reaching down his gun*). Maybe. (*Dog barks again.*)

EMMA (*coming in with water*). Mother, what's Rover barking at? (*She pauses just inside, listening. There is a long, clear wolf howl from far off. The dog barks vehemently as* ROBBIN *comes in. They all pause, looking at each other, listening. Another howl.*)

ROBBIN. Wolves.

TOMMY (*stopping in doorway*). Kumo says the Utahs sometimes make the wolf call.

ROBBIN. When they're sneaking up on somebody.

TOMMY. For signals, too, when they're stealing cattle. (JOE *cocks his gun. The others go to the barrel and empty their buckets. As* MOTHER *is lighting the candles, there is another long howl.* ALL *stop, facing each other, listening. . . . The cry is answered.* JOE *moves to the window. The dog seems terrified, barking.*)

MOTHER. Does it sound like wolves, Joe?

JOE (*nodding, his head cocked*). It sounds like wolves. (*Looking closer into the dusk.*) There's something moving on the horizon! (ROBBIN *climbs up on the chest, kneels there by* JOE, *looking out.* EMMA *moves to* MOTHER. TOMMY *runs to the little opening UR. Just then another cry chills them. They listen. The cry is taken up by one echo, then another,* seeming to run a wide circle round the house. The window shutter bangs, the candles flicker, almost go out. EMMA screams softly. MOTHER hurries to door.)

MOTHER. Mary! Jane! (As JANE whisks MARY inside, MOTHER shuts the door. The children pull in toward her, as if hunting the light. JOE goes to the door, hesitates, then opens it and starts out.)

JANE. Don't go, Joe! Maybe it's wolves, and maybe—

TOMMY (at lookout window). There's something moving out there on the ridge.

ROBBIN. I see it! Against the glow in the west.

JOE (starting out again). I'm going to find out.

JANE. Duck, Joe! They'll see you against the light.

MOTHER (trying to keep steady). Oh, it's probably only wolves.

JOE (rifle to shoulder). We'll see.

MOTHER (impulsively). Challenge first, Joe!

JOE. And let them get the drop on me?

MOTHER. It's only fair to call a warning—

JOE. Well—seems like just asking for trouble. . . . Hello! (No answer.) Hello! (A long silence, all waiting, watching.) There's something behind that big rock. . . . Who's there? (For answer, a shot rings out. JOE jumps, flings his gun in the air and falls backward in the doorway. There is a full-throated war whoop off. JANE leaps to JOE's side.)

JANE. Joe!

TOMMY. Indians! (He bangs the shutter and bars it.)

MOTHER. Emma—the bedroom! Bar the shutters! (EMMA and TOMMY dash for the bedroom, as MOTHER rushes to help JANE drag JOE inside and bar the door. During all this there has been accelerating gunfire outside and a gradual increase in number and volume of war whoops, which seem to grow and spread around the house. TOMMY stands in the doorway L, as the dog barks and then yelps as if hit when a gun fires close by. Crying out, TOMMY runs to JOE where he lies on the floor, takes the pistol from JOE's holster.)

TOMMY. Rover! They've shot my dog! (He rushes to the lookout window and starts to fire out of it.)

JANE (suddenly remembering). Oh—the rifle—we've lost Joe's gun! (She dashes to door, unbars it in a frantic effort to retrieve JOE's rifle; but MOTHER is there to stop her. Pushing JANE away, she fastens the door securely, runs to the chimney corner, grabs the shotgun, hurries back near the door R, removes a chink from between the logs, thrusts the gun through and commences firing out. On a confusion of vigilant watching and firing through cracks, with gunfire off, as well as inside, and with yelping and howling—

CURTAIN

ACT TWO

SCENE: The Leigh ranch interior again. The second night of the siege. The wounded man has been fixed more comfortably on the top of the cellar door. His arm is in a sling and his shoulder is bandaged. JANE is lifting his head, giving him water. On the table which has been pushed against the wall L, TOMMY kneels, peering out through a hole made by removing a chink there. MOTHER leans against door R, with shotgun in hand, almost asleep. EMMA is asleep in the rocker by the fireplace.

JOE (as JANE tries to make him more comfortable). Oh-oh!

JANE Take it easy, Joe. (She goes to fire, gets basin of hot water and sets it near JOE. Begins to work on his shoulder, loosening the bandages. JOE is now facing front. He sees TOMMY.)

JOE. See anything, Tommy?

TOMMY. It's pretty dark. I can hardly see the corral.

JANE (taking a cloth). This waiting is worse than fighting.

TOMMY. Yeah—every time they attack you wish they'd stop—and—

JANE. And every time they stop, you wonder—

TOMMY. You almost wish something would happen.

JANE (cleaning around the wound; JOE groans). Something has happened!

TOMMY (looks at JOE, then—). I wonder why they stopped shooting?

JANE. Probably trying to decide what to do with us. (She begins to redress JOE's shoulder.)

JOE. Or else they're too busy roasting our cattle and feasting.

TOMMY. Do you think they could be out of bullets?

JOE. Or just saving them.

TOMMY. Till they figure out some way to get us?

JOE. They don't know how little ammunition we've got, remember.

TOMMY. Maybe they've wondered why we didn't shoot more, whenever they attacked.

JANE (who has finished with JOE, setting the basin down). If only we could get some sleep. Mother! You're asleep standing up. (MOTHER jumps, and JANE goes to her.) Go in and lie down with Robbin and Mary.

MOTHER (shivering, rubbing her eyes and yawning). What time is it?

JANE (*turning to* TOMMY *as* JOE *rises on one elbow*). Tommy?

TOMMY (*getting out his watch and squinting at it*). It's half-past— It's stopped! (TOMMY *pockets his watch disgustedly, turns back to the hole and looks out.*) Must be nearly midnight.

JANE. Seems like a month since Father left.

TOMMY. And this is only the second night.

JANE. He said he would be gone three. . . . I wonder how long you can keep awake, in danger?

MOTHER (*shivers again*). Stir the fire, Tommy.

JANE. There's not much wood left.

MOTHER (*moving over to cover up* EMMA). Look at the children, Jane. (*She goes to window UL, tries to see out through a crack in the shutter.* JANE *goes into bedroom, then comes back and at a low moan from* JOE, *takes him more water.*)

JANE (*whispers, worried, to* MOTHER). He's burning up.

MOTHER. How much water left?

JANE. In case of a long siege— (*She shakes her head.*)

TOMMY. If only we could see out. I believe I could make it to the spring—

MOTHER. No, Tommy. We can't risk that until absolutely necessary. We still have a *little* water.

JANE. They're crafty—these Utahs. Probably hiding out there, just waiting for us to make a mistake.

TOMMY. They'd like us to think they're gone, so we'll come out. (*He looks out again cautiously.*) If only we hadn't lost Joe's rifle. (*Inspecting the pistol in his hand.*) Every time I've seen one of them, he's been too far off for this, or so close to the house I could see only his tail feathers. If I had a rifle—

ACT TWO   165

JANE. Oh, if there were only some way of getting word to
Father! (JOE is mumbling—half asleep, half delirious.)
TOMMY. Some day we'll be able to send messages through
the air . . . Like they're doing back East already.
JANE. A good homing pigeon would do right now.
TOMMY (after a pause). Noah had one.
JANE (sleepily). Who?
TOMMY. Noah. (JANE looks puzzled.) In the Ark, you know.
JANE (absentmindedly). Oh.
TOMMY. We could have sent Rover—
JANE. Don't feel bad, Tom. Maybe they didn't kill your dog.
TOMMY. You think so? (EMMA cries out in her sleep and
looks up. MOTHER moves quickly to her.)
MOTHER. Sh-sh-sh! Emma dear, everything's all right.
EMMA. Where's Papa? (Looking around, frightened.) Hasn't
he come yet?
MOTHER. Not yet, dear. . . . Jane, go with her into the bed-
room.
EMMA. No! It's dark in there! . . . I don't want to, Mother.
(There is an answering cry from the bedroom. The door
opens, and MARY, still dressed, comes in fearfully, followed
by ROBBIN.)
JANE (running to quiet her). Mary! Mary!
MARY. Where's Papa?
JANE. Hush! (Indicating Indians may be listening.) We have
to be quiet.
MARY. But I saw an Indian. (Almost crying.) He came right
through the window.
MOTHER (sits in the rocker as EMMA rises, taking MARY in
her lap). No, baby. We haven't seen an Indian for hours.
MARY. Why can't we have more light?

MOTHER. Because the Indians could see us through the cracks then.

ROBBIN (*coming to* MOTHER, *rubbing his eyes*). Is it still night?

MOTHER. Yes, son—or early morning.

ROBBIN. I'm so tired . . . Could I have a drink?

MOTHER. We've saving the water as long as we can. . . . Couldn't you get some more sleep, Robby?

ROBBIN. Well, Mary kept me awake for a long time.

MARY. It was dark in there, and—and—

ROBBIN. She kept seeing black things in the corner.

MARY. Well—

ROBBIN. That's why I had to open the door a crack for her.

MOTHER (*putting a shawl around* MARY). That's fine of you, son—to watch out for your little sister.

ROBBIN. She was afraid.

MARY. So was Robbin.

MOTHER. Sh-sh! Robbin's a big man. We know there's nothing in the corner, don't we, son? (*She puts her arm around* ROBBIN.)

ROBBIN. Um-hum.

MOTHER. Of course.

ROBBIN. But, Mother—a funny thing—even when you know there's nothing there, it's there just the same. (MOTHER *laughs in spite of her weariness and anxiety, pulls him closer. The others look amused, all but* MARY *who is serious about it.* . . . MOTHER *rises, taking* MARY *by the hand.*)

MOTHER. Come on, dear, let's make sure there's no Indian and see if we can't get some more sleep.

MARY. Well—if you'll sleep with us, Mother.

MOTHER. Come along, Mary. Let's find the sandman, Robbin. Then you'll be wide awake when daylight comes, so you can watch while we rest.

ROBBIN. Doesn't Tommy have to sleep?

TOMMY. Oh, I'm not sleepy. You sleep first.

MOTHER. We'll see, son.

TOMMY (as they start into the bedroom). Mother, is it all right—I think if I could have a drink of water, I could keep awake better?

MOTHER. Look and see, son. (TOMMY goes to the barrel, looks in, takes dipper and is about to drink. Hesitates, looks at JANE who gives him a look of deep sympathy. Pouring the water back, TOMMY renews his watch at the table.)

TOMMY. Oh, I guess I'm not very thirsty after all.

EMMA (who has been leaning up against window, rouses again, comes back to rocker). Why doesn't Papa come?

TOMMY. Don't worry, Emma; he'll come.

EMMA. I wish something would happen.

TOMMY. So do I. (Looking out.) This waiting— Say! Something is happening!

EMMA. Huh? (She jumps up beside TOMMY and tries to see.)

TOMMY. Something—there's something moving out there.

EMMA. Where?

TOMMY. Look—there—right by the corral.

EMMA. Where? Where is it?

TOMMY. Don't you—

EMMA. Sure, I see it—it's moving!

TOMMY. Crawling along.

EMMA. It's an Indian!

TOMMY. Yeah—he's coming toward the house.

EMMA (getting to the floor). Sh-shall I call Mother?

TOMMY. Not yet! Let's see what he's up to. Look, he's going

to the window. (*They both slip down and run to window,
waiting.*)

INDIAN (*outside*). Hol-la!—White man—

EMMA. What do you think he wants? (TOMMY *shakes his
head.*)

INDIAN. Hol-la! John Leigh. Mike-tickaboo!

EMMA. He's calling Papa.—Let's get Mama!

TOMMY (*holding her*). The dirty lizard! He knows Papa's
not here. That's why they attacked us in the first place.

INDIAN. At-am-bar! Me talk?

TOMMY. He wants to talk with Papa. The dirty— (INDIAN
rattles shutters.)

JANE (*as* EMMA *jumps and screams softly, wakes up*). Oh,
what's the— Tommy, what is it?

INDIAN. White squaw, you talk. Peshadny!

JANE (*taking shotgun, hurries to window, with finger-to-lip
motion*). Sh-sh!

INDIAN. White squaw, you speak open door. Tsap-kak!

JANE (*looking toward inner room, as if about to call* MOTHER,
suddenly goes and kneels by JOE. *Shakes him.*) Joe! Joe!
(JOE *groans.*) Sh-sh-sh!

INDIAN. White man's squaw, you speak to Indian. Peshadny!
Me come in.

JANE. Joe! Joe! You've got to do it. You've got to wake up.

JOE (*opening his eyes*). What?

JANE. The Indians—they're trying to find out how we are!

INDIAN. Hol-la! White man no scare. Tsap-kak.

JANE. He's trying to find out if you're still alive, Joe. Answer
him. (JOE *doesn't seem to understand.*) Answer him!
(JOE *sits up, shaking his head.*)

INDIAN (*shaking shutters again*). White man no scare. (*Pause.*)
Me come in. Tsap-kak!

MOTHER (*appearing in door, L, blinking*). Goodness, what is it?

INDIAN (*at the door now*). White squaw Leigh—Tick-i. Me hungry, me cold. Me come in. (MOTHER *moves silently to the door, listens.*)

TOMMY. He says he wants meat—he's hungry.

JOE (*striving to hold steady*). How many shells for the shot-gun?

JANE. Only four.

JOE (*to* TOMMY). And the pistol?

TOMMY. Just a few more shots.

JOE. Then we can't hold out much longer. (*He seems very ill. Lies down.*)

MOTHER (*taking shotgun from fireplace, where* JANE *stood it earlier and going back to door*). We have to hold out.

INDIAN. Joe! You let Pah-Ute come in, Joe. Me Pah-Ute.

EMMA. Mama, he says he's Pah-Ute. Maybe—

INDIAN. Me tickaboo! Me Pah-Ute.

JANE. Maybe he *is* Pah-Ute.

EMMA. If he's Pah-Ute, he's friendly. Nearly always they are! Maybe he wants to help us—

INDIAN. Poo-suds—way-ah! You know, me Pah-Ute. Me hungry. Me cold. You give bread. Prowa! Me heap cold, want matches.

TOMMY. He wants matches.

EMMA. Mama, maybe he is cold. (*She moves swiftly to shelf L, and is about to get matches.*) Maybe we ought to give him matches to make a fire—

JOE (*rising again*). And set fire to the house. (EMMA *stops, turns, listening.*)

INDIAN. Coo-nah, you make fire!

JANE. But he sounds friendly. Maybe if we let him in—

We've always been friendly with the Indians. Why should they want to harm us? Maybe it's all a mistake. Maybe—

JOE. Mistake? (*Pointing to shoulder.*) This, you mean?

JANE. But you said yourself— Mother, we can't hold out much longer. If we don't let him in, and they renew the attack—

MOTHER (*nodding*). They'll be still more angry when they do break in.

JANE. But when our ammunition is gone we'll be at their mercy. What do you think?

INDIAN. White squaw, you open door for Pah-Ute. Me ticka-boo—to-witch-ee tick-a-boo!

JANE. What do you think?

MOTHER. I think he is a crafty liar, that's what I think. He is not hungry, nor are his fellows. They have taken our cattle, chickens, everything. He is no Pah-Ute, either. He sounds like a Utah to me.

INDIAN (*now back at window near which* TOMMY *and* EMMA *stand*). Coo-nah!

EMMA (*jumping in panic*). Mother!

MOTHER (*meeting her, shaking her*). Hush-sh! Never let an Indian know you're afraid. (*Moving to window.*) We'll fight as long as there is one shot left, and trust in God.

TOMMY. Then tell him, Ma.

EMMA. Tell him! (*She whispers it, bravely.*)

INDIAN. Tsap-kak. You let Pah-Ute come in? To-witch-ee tick-a-boo!

MOTHER (*louder*). No! You are not Pah-Ute! Ish-ump! You lie! You are not tickaboo! You are not friend. You have forked tongue. We will not open the door, and if you come in here, we will shoot you!

INDIAN (*laughing loudly*). Ho-oh! Oh, squaw shoot! (*His

laughter is shared by another rough voice, and then an-
other, and another, till it sounds as if the house were sur-
rounded by them.) Squaw shoot! Now me scare!

SECOND INDIAN. Now we heap scare!

THIRD INDIAN. Co-que!

FOURTH INDIAN. Co-que!

FIFTH INDIAN. Co-que!

SECOND INDIAN. White squaw me scare!

FIRST INDIAN. Me no scare for white man. White man coward! White man dead. E-iqueay! *(More laughter.)*

JANE. Joe, Joe, you answer them. They want to know how
strong we are. Don't let them know you're down. Joe!
(The voices outside rise in coarse laughter.)

JOE *(making great effort, rising on elbow).* Go away, you
coyotes! *(All listen, but there is no reply. JOE sinks down
again. All watch and listen anxiously.)*

TOMMY *(at chink over table).* There's something—I believe
I can see something moving by the corral.

EMMA. What is it? Where?

JANE *(beside him).* Maybe they're going away.

MOTHER *(goes to look).* Yes, but they'll come back.

TOMMY. They'll try to catch us off guard.

MOTHER. We can't let them catch us napping. *(She goes into
the other room. They check the bars, vigilant. JANE covers
JOE and feels his forehead, then goes back to her post and
looks out.)*

EMMA. Do you think Papa might get worried—and come
back before he planned?

JANE. It's our only hope, Emma.

TOMMY. He'll be disappointed to hear the Utahs stole the
cows and—and—

EMMA. And your pinto pony.

TOMMY. Now Jacob can't use my pony to trade for Kumo.
. . . And Rover . . .

JANE. Don't think about it, Tommy dear. Maybe Rover got
away. And Jacob will know what to do about Kumo.

EMMA (*sighing sleepily, curling up in the chair*). What time
is it?

TOMMY (*looking at watch*). It's half-past— My gosh, I forgot!
It was that time hours ago. (*Winds it.*)

JANE. It must be past midnight. (*Wearily stands by door
fighting to keep awake.*)

TOMMY. Why do you suppose they are quiet so long?

JANE. Just get ready, Tom; we'll know soon enough.

TOMMY. What do you think they did with Kumo?

JANE. Nothing bad, I hope.

TOMMY. I've got a hunch he's in Wah-karrah's wickiup right
now. (*He turns away from the crack, thinking. . . . Gradually, he slumps over on the table and sleeps.* JANE *alone
is watching. Finally she leans back in the corner and shuts
her eyes. As she dozes, a tiny puff of white smoke comes
from the crack under the door behind her. Then another
from between the logs behind the cupboard. She opens her
eyes intuitively, looks at* TOMMY *sleepily. Suddenly her
head jerks and she stands rigid, speechless, staring at the
hole in the wall; for as she is looking at* TOMMY, *a hand
comes through the chink by his head.*)

JANE. Tommy! (TOMMY *jumps. The hand disappears.*)

TOMMY (*pointing to the door*). Smoke! (*There is a sound outside the door. As* JANE *looks that way, another puff of
white smoke comes from the crack under the door.* JANE
*catches her breath, jumps into center of the room.
Watches. Another puff.*)

JANE. Mother!

EMMA (*rousing*). Mama, they're setting the house afire!

MOTHER (*coming in from bedroom, sees smoke*). The crafty—
That's why they wanted matches! Get ready! (*She grabs a
bucket and dips it full of water from the barrel as* MARY
comes softly in from the bedroom, followed by ROBBIN.)
Hush! Mary, you stand in the bedroom door and watch.
Robbin, you and Emma get some cloths—some burlap
from the bedroom floor, Emma! (*As* EMMA *runs for it,
she grabs the rag rug from the floor and dips it in water,
wrings it out.* EMMA *comes back with sacks.* MOTHER *dips
them quickly and hands some to* ROBBIN, *some to* EMMA.)
Now, stand ready, and if the flames come through, keep
them from spreading inside. Jane, keep us covered. They'll
probably attack if the fire catches on. Tommy, shoot out
the other side to draw their attention away from the door.
Wait—here, Emma, Robbin, bring water. (*She rushes to
hand them buckets which they hastily fill at the barrel.
Then she stands by the door, ready to open the top section
of it.*) Ready? (*She looks at all of them.*) Tommy, shoot!
(*As* TOMMY *commences to fire, she opens the door cautiously, peers out, then flings it wide and throws water on
the fire below. Hands bucket to* ROBBIN, *who scuttles for
more, as she throws his bucketful out. Then she throws*
EMMA'S, *while* EMMA *goes for more.* EMMA *grabs the
bucket with buttermilk.*)

EMMA. Mother, the water's almost gone, but throw this buttermilk on it. (*Just then there is a wild yell outside and an*
INDIAN *appears, but* MOTHER *shuts door with a bang and
bars it.* TOMMY *ceases fire.*)

MOTHER. There! . . . (*Seeing smoke still coming from behind cupboard, she grabs* EMMA'S *bucket and is starting to
throw contents through chinks behind cupboard when*

INDIAN *shakes door. Another shakes window UL. There is a shot from outside.*) Keep down! (*Another shot.*)

TOMMY (*looking out*). Oh, look!

JANE. What?

MOTHER. What is it? (*Setting buttermilk down, L.*)

TOMMY. He's carrying a firebrand.

EMMA, ROBBIN. A firebrand?

MARY (*jumping away from window*). Mother!

MOTHER (*taking shotgun from* JANE). Keep the wet cloths ready, and watch. I'll see if I can get a shot at him from the bedroom window. (*Going.*)

TOMMY. He's going to the window! (*He jumps off table and starts for window, looking at pistol.*) We can't spare any more bullets.

JANE. I wish we could spare some more water!

TOMMY. Yeah. (*He notices the open keg with the buttermilk. Picks it up.*)

JANE. Oh, Tommy! We'll need that to drink.

TOMMY (*looking at contents*). Blue buttermilk?

JANE (*running to window*). Here, give me your gun. (EMMA *runs to assist them. The two girls are on either side of the window, waiting.* TOMMY *has the small keg poised, ready.* JANE *peers out crack, suddenly throws window open.*) Throw it! (*A feathered head disappears swiftly below window and, as* TOMMY *lets fly the sour liquid, there is a surprised and enraged protest from outside. But the window shuts off the view, and* EMMA *and* JANE *have it barred in a flash.* EMMA *springs back to the crack and looks out.*)

EMMA. Oh, look, it's put his fire out!

ROBBIN. Sure enough.

JOE (*rousing*). Good. Saved us a bullet.

TOMMY. And some water, too.

JANE. Maybe Tickaboo is really cold, now.

TOMMY (*suddenly folding arms, Indian fashion, and imitating the voice from outside*). "Tick-i! Me hungry."

JANE (*imitating him*). "Tsap kak! Open door."

EMMA (*falling in with them*). "Coo-nah! Fire." (*They all look at one another, drawn up in a row, then burst out laughing, a sort of explosion of relief, just as* MOTHER *reappears, L.*)

MOTHER. You shouldn't have done that. (*Crossing to inspect walls, R, and doorway.*) Too dangerous. They'll want revenge.

JANE. Yes, that'll hurt their pride more than a bullet would. (*As* JOE *coughs in pain.*) That smoke!

JOE (*coughing*). Terrible. (MARY *coughs, then* EMMA.)

EMMA (*looks wistfully into barrel*). If only we had more water.

MARY. Couldn't I have some water?

MOTHER. Yes, Mary; but if you have it now, there'll be none left for later.

EMMA. If only we hadn't had to use so much on the fire.

JANE. And to think they probably started the fire with matches they stole from us.

EMMA. Mama, why didn't the house catch on fire?

ROBBIN. Maybe they just wanted to smoke us out.

TOMMY (*on the table, suddenly*). Say, I'll bet I know why that fire put out so much smoke!

EMMA. Why? Because the house is wet and—

TOMMY. Sure, that's where the snow was. And that isn't all—

EMMA. Why did they start it on the wet side?

TOMMY. Because the wind's blowing from that side.

MOTHER (*after a pause*). What do you see now, Tommy?

TOMMY (*looking*). Not a thing.

MARY. Mother, I'm so thirsty—so hot. (MOTHER *goes to her, at rocker, C, and feels her forehead.* JANE *looks at her questioningly.* MOTHER *nods.* MARY *sees them and reacts fearfully.*) Mother! Have I got a fever?

MOTHER (*taking her in her lap*). Now, dear, you just shut your eyes and rest awhile. You'll be all right. (*Begins to rock and try to comfort her. Looks at the window.*) Jane. (JANE *goes and watches.*) Emma. (*She nods toward door,* L. EMMA *goes and stands watching.* MOTHER *croons softly to* MARY.)

MARY (*coughing*). But, Mother, I'm just terribly thirsty— couldn't you— (*Breaks off, coughing.*)

MOTHER. I know. But just try to forget. Try to sleep.

ROBBIN (*coughing, rubbing his eyes*). Isn't there some way we could get some water? That smoke makes me so thirsty.

MOTHER. It wouldn't be safe, son.

ROBBIN. Couldn't we sneak out when they're not looking?

MARY (*crying*). I want Papa. When's Papa coming home?

JOE (*starting up*). Oh-oh! (*Sinks down again.*)

EMMA. Mama, what'll we do if we don't get some water?

JANE (*she had been watching* JOE). Mama, we've just got to get word to Father, that's all.

MOTHER. Yes, daughter, but how?

JANE (*trying not to let* JOE *hear*). And we've got to get a doctor for Joe! (*There is a tense pause.*)

TOMMY. Mama—I'm going after Papa!

MOTHER (*surprised*). Oh, Tommy—

JANE (*seeing he is deadly earnest*). No. You can't go, Tommy!

EMMA (*impulsively*). They'd get you, Tommy.

MOTHER. No, son—you musn't think of it.

TOMMY. Look—this is the second night, and Father may not be home until after another one—

MOTHER. I know, son, but—

TOMMY. Our food's gone.

MOTHER. Yes.

TOMMY. And our water.

MOTHER. I know.

TOMMY. And our bullets, almost.

MOTHER. Almost.

TOMMY. And if the wind changes, or the house dries out—

ROBBIN (*impulsively*). They'll burn us up!

MOTHER. Hush, Robbin! (*To* TOMMY.) I know, my son. We just have to risk it.

TOMMY. Maybe Father will never get here, and—

MOTHER (*quickly*). Of course he'll get here!

TOMMY. But someone ought to warn him, so—

ROBBIN. So he won't walk into an Indian trap!

EMMA. He won't know the Indians are here, will he?

ROBBIN. No.

EMMA. Then he won't bring help, and the Utahs will—

MOTHER. Hush, child! (*Then wearily, uncertainly—*) He'll be all right.

TOMMY. But how can we last till he comes? We're worn out and have nothing to fight with.

ROBBIN. But Papa will bring us ammunition!

TOMMY. And a lot of good that'll do, if he can't get in when he comes.

ROBBIN. He could come through the secret passage!

TOMMY. If it wasn't surrounded—

ROBBIN. Well, he could—

TOMMY. And if we *could* wait— Mother, let me go. I know I could get through to the fort—I just *know* I could!

MOTHER. Oh, Tommy boy—

TOMMY. I won't go on the trail, Ma; I'll keep in the forest till I'm away from here, then I'll strike out across country.

MOTHER. But think of the danger—

TOMMY. They'll never see me, Mother, never!

MOTHER. No.

TOMMY (*very firm*). Well—then instead of risking one of us, we risk— (*He breaks off and looks around at them all.*)

MOTHER (*miserable, seeking advice*). Jane?

JANE (*suddenly kneeling down and hugging* TOMMY). Oh, Tommy, darling, we just can't spare you. (*She is in tears.* MARY *starts to cry.* ROBBIN *rubs his eyes.* EMMA *takes a handkerchief.*)

TOMMY. But, Jane, don't you see— (*Again he looks at the* CHILDREN.)

MOTHER. Hush, Mary! They'll hear you. Mustn't let them know you're afraid. Pioneers have to be brave. (*Looking decisively at* JANE, *stands and puts* MARY *down.*) Jane, perhaps—God is with the boy, Jane. Perhaps he's right. Surely the Lord will be with him.

TOMMY. Oh, good, Mother! (*He begins to hustle his things together—his hat from the rack, L, his knife from the shelf.* MOTHER *goes into bedroom.*)

ROBBIN. You'd better crawl till you get into the trees, Tommy.

TOMMY. When I get out of the shed, I'll go along behind the thicket.

EMMA. If only the Indians hadn't stolen your horse.

TOMMY (*sadly*). I'd be glad for even a—dog to go with me.

ROBBIN. I'll go with you, Tom! (*Looks at* MOTHER *excitedly as she emerges from bedroom with* TOMMY'S *coat and scarf.*) Could I, Mother?

MOTHER. Oh, no, Robby.

JANE (*quickly*). One will have a much greater chance of getting through, Robbin.

ROBBIN. But one of us would be bound to get through—

TOMMY (*as* MOTHER *helps him into his coat*). I'll be all right; don't worry. I know some Indian tricks.

ROBBIN. How to throw them off the track, like Kumo showed us.

TOMMY (*smiling, going toward cellar door*). Sure.

JOE (*rousing*). You going through here?

TOMMY. Through the cellar and—

JOE. And if they catch you coming out of the shed—

ROBBIN. They'll find the secret passage and come through!

TOMMY. Well—

JOE. Out the window, then we can keep you covered—if we can see you.

EMMA (*looking through a crack, L*). The stars seem a little brighter now. (TOMMY *looks at the pistol, then hands it to* JOE. *He takes the tomahawk which* FATHER *took from Wan-tah, inspects it, is about to put it in his belt, notices* MOTHER's *shudder, puts it back.*)

MOTHER. Just trust in the Lord, son.

TOMMY (*at the window*). I will, Mother.

EMMA. If he goes out the window, the Indians will see him.

MOTHER. We'll put out the light while the window's open. (JANE *goes to the candle.* TOMMY *is ready. Suddenly,* TOMMY, *who was—for the moment's emergency—a man, feels himself a small boy again. He looks at* MOTHER, *rushes to her and buries his face on her shoulder.* MOTHER *kneels and indicates they are all to come to her. Silently, she bows her head in prayer. Then she rises and takes the shotgun and stands by the window. Looks at* TOMMY.) Look before you go out. (EMMA *stands ready to open the win-*

dow. JANE *is ready at the candle.* MOTHER *puts* TOMMY's *scarf on him.*) Tommy—remember: never show an Indian you're afraid!

ROBBIN. Tell Papa to bring guns and bullets!

MARY (*excited now*). And bring the whole militia!

MOTHER. Sh-sh! (*They all jump to their posts, looking out cautiously, listening.*) Jane! (JANE *dowses candle. Darkness.* MOTHER *opens window, peers out.*) See anything? (*They are all looking out. There is no reply.*) God bless you, my son. (TOMMY *goes out window. She stands a moment listening and watching.*)

ROBBIN (*at the peephole*). He's down! He's past the spring. He's gone! (*The window is shut, the candle lighted.* MOTHER *kneels facing the fireplace.* EMMA *and* MARY *huddle near her. Just then a shot rings out.* MOTHER *jumps to her feet.* JOE *looks alive.*)

MOTHER. Oh, Joe, was it—

JOE. No, I don't think they saw Tommy. That shot came through the shutter.

JANE. Then they know we opened it.

MOTHER. Get ready then. They're coming! (*They jump to their posts. More shots. Then a rattling of shutters.*)

EMMA (*looking out chink R, jumps away, screams*). Oh, he's got a pitchfork! (*As the door begins to give and a pitchfork shows through the crack—*) He's coming in!

MOTHER (*rushing to hold door shut*). Quick, Jane! Emma! The chest. (*All rush to the chest UL and help push it, but* MARY, *who runs to the wall, grabs tomahawk, and jumps upon chest brandishing tomahawk.* MOTHER *rushes back to get shotgun, turns and sees* MARY.) Mary—baby!

MARY. Now, just let 'em come!

CURTAIN

ACT THREE, Scene One

SCENE: An open place in the forest, not long after TOMMY *has left the ranch. It is dark, but for moon and starlight. There is a large boulder about C, and near it, two smaller ones.*

An INDIAN *stands with one foot on a rock, looking R, listening. As he moves R and looks off, we can see it is* WAN-TAH. *Evidently he hears something, turns and runs L and off.* TOMMY, *looking back over his shoulder, comes limping in from R, breathing hard. He is leading* ROVER. *He sits on the rock where* WAN-TAH *just stood and looks around suspiciously.*

TOMMY. We got away from them, Rover. (*Looking around again, patting dog.*) I'm glad they didn't shoot you. Gosh, the woods are full of Utahs! (*He searches his pockets, looking around for Indians meanwhile, takes out a pencil.*) So I guess you got to be a carrier pigeon, old boy. (*He brings out a piece of brown paper from coat pocket. Writes.*) I may—be captured—by Utahs. Send—help—to my—folks. Signed—Tommy Leigh. (*Searches pockets again, brings out cartridge shell. Holds it up, looking at it. Rolls the note and slips it in shell.*) There, that'll do it. (*Fishes out a piece of string, fastens the note on* ROVER's *collar.*) There. Now, old boy, you'll have to do the rest. (*Rises, leads* ROVER L.) Go to the fort, Rover. (*Shoves him out and waves after him.*) Go on! Go to the fort, Rover. Go on! (TOMMY *stands for a moment waving, then goes back to the rock. Sits. Takes off shoe, shakes it. Looks behind rock suspiciously. Seems to see something R. Puts shoe on, then ducking low, slips out L. Immediately he comes back,* looking apprehensively over his shoulder. Seems to see something, darts to boulder and hides behind it. WAN-TAH's head appears above a boulder L. TOMMY ducks. WAN-TAH crawls toward the big boulder, keeping in the shadow. TOMMY manages to keep the boulder between them. Finally PIANG-KA's head appears above the boulder on which TOMMY sat. As TOMMY backs away from WAN-TAH, PIANG-KA grabs him from behind and pins his arms down. WAN-TAH whips out a thong and ties TOMMY's wrists in front. TOMMY struggles and kicks.)

WAN-TAH (raising his knife). Shin-nob! No tang-i! (To PIANG-KA.) Pah-Ute papoose! Punkerro! (PIANG-KA goes off L quickly. WAN-TAH goes over TOMMY for weapons. Finds the watch. Holds it up, admiring it as PIANG-KA comes back with KUMO, whose arms are bound behind him. TOMMY, surprised, is about to speak but KUMO shakes head. TOMMY assumes poker face.)

PIANG-KA (admiring watch). Ummh! Wah-pana-karra?

WAN-TAH (putting it to his ear). Hum-pah?

PIANG-KA. Hum-pah? (Holds out hand.) Mug-gi!

WAN-TAH (handing it over). Nan-kuh-bah. (Makes sign for ear-listen.)

PIANG-KA (listens delightedly, looks at watch). Wah-pana-karra!

TOMMY. Wah-pana-karra—sure it's gold. It's a watch. My grandfather—

WAN-TAH (raising his hand, menacing). No at-am-bar!

PIANG-KA (puts watch in his pouch as he takes mirror from it). Poon-e-kee!

WAN-TAH. Hum-pah?

PIANG-KA (making sign for mirror). Nau-voo-nump!

WAN-TAH (*admiring himself in mirror*). Nau-voo-nump! Ummh . . .

TOMMY. Why, that's my— You stole that from my mother!

WAN-TAH (*menacing*). Shin-nob! (*While the two* INDIANS *have been looking at mirror,* KUMO *has managed to wriggle one hand free enough to steal the watch from* PIANG-KA'S *pouch. He slips out L. When the* INDIANS *discover* KUMO *is gone,* WAN-TAH *lets out a yelp and starts out L after him.* PIANG-KA *struggles with* TOMMY *and finally lashes him to the rock and goes out after* WAN-TAH. TOMMY *looks around, then up at the stars. Tries his bonds. Just then* KUMO'S *head appears from behind the boulder. When he taps* TOMMY *on the shoulder,* TOMMY *almost yells. But* KUMO *shakes his head vigorously. Then with a grunt he indicates his bound hands, then backs around so* TOMMY *can untie them with his fingers. When* KUMO *is free, he looses* TOMMY *from the boulder and frees his wrists.*)

TOMMY (*looking around*). Now, let's go! (KUMO *shakes head.*) Tammy-nah-wah! (KUMO, *looking L, puts finger to lips, grabs* TOMMY *and pushes him against the rock at spot where he was bound, then jumps back of it himself—just in time, as* PIANG-KA *comes into view L.* TOMMY *stands looking elaborately innocent. When* PIANG-KA *has gone R,* KUMO *emerges, holding out his tunic to* TOMMY. *Surprised,* TOMMY *starts to question, but the Indian boy's finger-to-lips stops him, and then* KUMO *begins to take* TOMMY'S *coat off.*)

KUMO. Pe-mo! (TOMMY *gets the idea, takes off coat. In a moment they are in each other's clothes. Their trousers, both of buckskin, do not need to be exchanged.* KUMO *takes out the gold watch, listens to it tick, gives it to* TOMMY.)

TOMMY (*taking it delightedly*). My watch!

KUMO. Oo-ah.

TOMMY. Where did— How did you get it?

KUMO. Ne-ab. Me take.

TOMMY. You mean . . . ?

KUMO (*nods*). You go. (*Pointing off L, pushing him.*)

TOMMY. Come with me— Tammy-nah-wah!

KUMO (*grabbing thongs and thrusting them at* TOMMY). Ta-peech-e!

TOMMY. You mean—you want me to tie you up—in my place? (*He pantomimes the idea.* KUMO *nods.*) I'll make it loose. (*Ties* KUMO's *wrists in front.*)

KUMO (*grinning*). Kumo get loose. Pi-queay. (*Gesturing L.*) You go! Tum-by-o!

TOMMY. All right, I'll go to the fort and get help.

KUMO (*nods vigorously*). Katz-oats. (*He indicates* TOMMY's *hat.*) Yenno!

TOMMY (*does not understand at first; looks behind him to see what* KUMO *is nodding at; finally understands*). Oh, my hat. (*Takes off* KUMO's *headband and claps his hat on* KUMO.) If you don't escape, we'll come after you.

KUMO. Pi-queay! (*Trying to shove* TOMMY *off as he looks L.* TOMMY *looks L, then abruptly ducks behind the boulder as* WAN-TAH *comes into view L.* WAN-TAH *looks at* KUMO. KUMO *ducks his head, so that the hat will shadow his face.* WAN-TAH *comes nearer and when his back is turned,* TOMMY *slips out back of him L.* WAN-TAH *goes out R.* KUMO *looks up to see* TOMMY *coming back.*)

TOMMY. You go with me, Kumo. Tammy-nah-wah!

KUMO. No Tammy-nah-wah. You go quick. (*As* TOMMY *hesitates.*) Bring guns. Bring Jacob. Pun-kerro! (KUMO *starts to shove* TOMMY, *but sees* WAN-TAH *coming R. He seizes* TOMMY *and pulls him down behind the rock, where they both hide.* WAN-TAH *sees that* TOMMY *has gone, comes over to inspect. When he is almost on top of them,* KUMO, *dressed as* TOMMY, *springs into the air, and runs R.* WAN-TAH, *startled, lets out a yelp and pursues. As they go out,* PIANG-KA *appears and races after them.* TOMMY *then jumps up and runs off L.)*

CURTAIN

ACT THREE, Scene Two

SCENE: *The Leigh ranch a little later, just before dawn.*

ROBBIN *and* MARY *are asleep near the fire, close to* JOE. EMMA *sleeps in the chair. They are covered with blankets.* MOTHER *stands by the door, trying to see out.* JANE *is by the window, dozing against the wall.* MARY *coughs in her sleep, cries out, rises, coughing.* ROBBIN *starts and sits up; then,* EMMA.

MOTHER (*going to her*). Sh-sh-sh, Mary! Keep the cover on, dear. (JANE *rouses, looks at them.*)

MARY (*fretfully*). I want a drink of water.

MOTHER (*feeling her forehead*). Hush, dear, just try to sleep.

JANE. Still hot? (As MOTHER *nods.*) It's the smoke. It's choked us all up.

MARY. A drink please, Mother.

ROBBIN. Can't we get some water, Mother?

JANE. How, Robbin?

ROBBIN. Two whole nights and a day! Can't we just try?

EMMA (*sitting up*). Are the Indians still there?

JANE (*looking out*). We don't know. We haven't seen one for a long time.

ROBBIN. Then we could go for water, couldn't we?

MARY. Someone get some water, please.

EMMA. Couldn't we, Mother?

MARY. Please, Mother—I'm so thirsty.

JANE. Stop it, Mary. They'll hear you.

JOE (*trying to get up*). Water! Oh! (*Groggily, as* JANE *goes to him.*) Water— I dreamed I saw a whole river—

JANE. No, Joe. Lie still. (*She puts her hand on his forehead.*) Mother, what shall we do?

MOTHER (*with sudden resolution, indicating that they are to look out*). See if you can see anything, Jane. Emma. (*She goes into bedroom.*) I'll look out from here. (JANE *and* EMMA *obey.* JANE *then goes to door, R, looks out through crack.* MOTHER *comes back.*) See anything?

JANE. Not a thing. But it's pretty dark.

EMMA. It's always darkest just before dawn.

JANE. They could be right against the house and we'd never see them.

ROBBIN. I wish daylight would come.

MARY. Where do you think Tommy is by now? I wish Papa would come.

ROBBIN. Then he could get us some water.

EMMA. But he may not come until tomorrow night.

MARY. Mother— (JOE *groans.* MOTHER *stands, C, uncertain. She and* JANE *exchange looks.*)

JANE (*looking out crack, uncertain*). It's awfully dark—

MOTHER. What do you think?

JANE. Well—it would be better to try now than after daylight. (*With decisive movements,* MOTHER *gets her coat from bedroom and then a pail from UL.* MOTHER *starts to put on her coat.*) No, Mother, I'll go! (*Trying to stop her mother.*)

MOTHER (*trying to push past her*). I couldn't let you, dear.

ROBBIN. Look, Mother, let me go. Then you and Jane can watch while I go after the water.

MOTHER. Oh, Robbin, child—

ROBBIN. You let Tommy go—

EMMA. Robbin's right, Mother—and I'll go with him. If you and Jane watch us and hold the door open, I'll bet we could make it to the spring and back before the Indians would notice us.

MOTHER (*as* ROBBIN *grabs the pail from her*). Robbin—

JANE. They're right, Mother—that's the best way.

ROBBIN (*putting the shotgun in her hand as* MOTHER *hesitates*). You keep us covered, Ma. We won't be afraid if you're watching.

EMMA (*starting for window UL,* ROBBIN *following*). How'll we get out? The window?

MOTHER. No, Emma, go out the door this time. (*She stands at door, trying to see out crack.*)

EMMA. But won't they—

MOTHER. We'll have to chance it. Jane, take the pistol. Watch the window. (*She takes hold of the chest that barricades the door. They all assist her cautiously. When they have removed the barricade to C,* MOTHER *stands at the door. She motions to* MARY. JANE *takes the pistol in one hand, the candle in the other.*) Mary, lie down by Joe. (MARY *does so.* JANE *moves to window.*) Now, are you ready? (EMMA *grabs another pail, kisses her mother on the cheek, as* MOTHER *cautiously slips the bar.*) God bless you. (JANE *has candle near the window.*) Jane! (*The light goes out. Sound of door and window being opened.* MOTHER *peers* out the partly open door, JANE out the window. MOTHER pushes ROBBIN and EMMA out.) Go quickly—quietly! (They go. MOTHER and JANE watch breathlessly.)

JANE (after a moment). Do you see anything?

MOTHER. No, but I hear them dipping water.

JANE. Oh, here they come— Here they come!

MOTHER. Keep your pistol ready. (While the light is still out, EMMA hurries in followed by ROBBIN who has ROVER by the collar. The door and window close. Bars are fastened and JANE lights the candle. EMMA takes ROBBIN's bucket to the water barrel.)

JANE. Oh, thank goodness! (She puts the candle on the mantel again.)

ROBBIN. Mother, look!

MARY. Oh, look! (Pointing to ROVER.)

JANE. Rover! How did he get—?

EMMA. He came to us at the spring.

ROBBIN (grabbing the dog's collar). Rover! Good old Rover! And we thought the Indians shot you.

MARY. Water! (She starts for the barrel.)

JANE (hurrying with cup to JOE). Joe, Joe! (He rouses, stupid, but when she puts the cup to his lips, drinks greedily.)

MOTHER (helping MARY with water, and taking a cupful to ROBBIN). Don't let him have too much at once, Jane.

ROBBIN (taking cup from MOTHER). Might make him sick.

EMMA. Water! (Takes another drink.) I didn't think plain water could be so wonderful.

JOE (reviving). Wonderful! (He leans back weakly.)

ROBBIN (putting down his cup and kneeling by ROVER). I'll say it's— Say— (He is staring at ROVER's collar.)

MOTHER. What is it, Robbin?

ROBBIN (*taking note from collar*). There's something on Rover's collar!

JANE, EMMA. What?

ROBBIN. It's Tommy's bullet whistle!

EMMA. Look—what's in it?

ROBBIN. It's a note. (*He has untied it and is opening it.*)

MARY. A note?

MOTHER (*reaching for it*). Let me see, son.

JANE. What is it, Mother?

MARY. What does it say?

MOTHER (*reading the note*). "If Rover gets in with this, you'll know I'm here. Just hold steady. Be careful. If I can't find some way to get in, I'll go back for help. Have Tommy unlock the cellar door and watch for me."

ROBBIN. Papa!

EMMA. Tommy—he doesn't know Tommy's gone!

JANE. Mother, do you suppose Tommy—

JOE (*weakly, but better*). Tommy just missed your father on the way, that's all.

JANE. But, if— Here, Joe. (*Helps JOE to rocking chair.*)

MOTHER. Robbin, unlock the outside cellar door. (ROBBIN *goes down cellar.*) Mary, take Rover into the other room. (*She stands dazed, uncertain what to do.*)

EMMA. You were wishing for a carrier pigeon, Jane!

MARY. Rover's better than a carrier pigeon! (*Taking* ROVER.)

EMMA. Well, that's once more we fooled the Utahs.

JANE. I wonder if they knew about the water.

EMMA. I thought I saw them in every shadow. (*There is a long-drawn-out hoot of an owl.* EMMA, JANE *and* MOTHER *listen.* MARY *appears in bedroom door, listening. The cellar lid rises swiftly and* ROBBIN *comes up.*) Robbin!

ROBBIN. I thought I heard— (*He breaks off, listening. There is another owl hoot.*) Papa! (*Dashing for the window.*)

MARY. It's Papa's signal! (*She follows* ROBBIN. *They listen.*)

EMMA. Do you think— (*The owl hoot is repeated.*)

ROBBIN. Shall I answer him?

MOTHER. Joe?

JOE. Sounds like an owl.

MARY. If it's Papa—

ROBBIN (*jumping to open the cellar door*). He said to open the cellar door!

JOE (*as* JANE *helps him to the cellar door*). Would he dare come up through here—with Indians—

ROBBIN (*as hoot is repeated once again, going to the crack L*). Hoooo-ooooot! Hoooo— (*The outside door begins to rattle.* MOTHER *and* JANE *jump toward it, ready for action.*)

MOTHER. The door!

EMMA. We forgot to barricade it again! (*There is a banging of bodies against the door.* MOTHER *and* JANE *brace against it.* JOE *tries to help but has to give up; stumbles back to chair. The door is giving.*)

ROBBIN. Oh, look, the bar is breaking.

MOTHER. Quick, Emma, Robbin—the cupboard! (EMMA *and* ROBBIN *rush to push up the cupboard. There is a terrible struggle, with the door opening a crack, and a hand coming through.* EMMA *runs to fire, grabs the poker and burns the hand, which is quickly withdrawn. There is a howl of pain. Someone starts working on the window again.* EMMA *runs to it. Their forces are divided between the door and window and they are unable to get the cupboard in front of the door. Then there is a rattling in the bedroom.*) Robbin, the bedroom! (ROBBIN *runs out L.*)

MARY (*who is near the fireplace, starts, then bangs down*

cellar door and jumps away). Mother! There's someone coming from the cellar! (ROBBIN stands in doorway L.)

JANE. Maybe it's Father.

EMMA (running to cellar door and looking in). Indians! (She bangs the lid on the cellar—backs away. MOTHER turns, with back pushing against door, and points shotgun toward trapdoor. JANE, near her, points pistol. EMMA, with poker, stands near fireplace, ready for action. Even JOE struggles to stand. There is a tense moment while the straining at door and window continues. Then a befeathered head appears as the cellar lid opens. MARY shrinks back against MOTHER. MOTHER takes aim. EMMA lifts poker. But the head emerges and the body stands straight. It is FATHER dressed in Indian clothes. He throws off headdress.)

EMMA. Father!

JANE. Father!

ROBBIN, MARY. Papa!

MOTHER, JOE. John! (MOTHER lowers her gun. There is a lurch against the door. The red arm comes in again. The shoulder is following. FATHER runs to the door, reaches through the space over the shoulder and there is a loud crack and a surprised yell as he hits the INDIAN. He pulls MARY away and helps push.)

FATHER (there is a shot outside). Duck! (They duck. There is another shot and FATHER grabs shotgun from MOTHER and aims it out crack. Fires. There is a terrific howl outside.) Robbin, get a hammer! Emma, some nails. (Hands gun back to MOTHER. They scurry to carry out his orders. He, JANE and MOTHER hold the door as the hammer and nails are brought. While they push against it, he drives in some nails. Then they move the cupboard in front of door. The firing and noise outside die down.)

MOTHER (*almost collapsing*). Oh, John! (FATHER *turns to her, but just then another shot rings out.*)

FATHER. Keep down, everybody. (*He begins to take fresh cartridges from a belt inside his Indian clothes.*) Joe, where's your— (*Notices* JOE's *bandages.*) What happened to you?

JOE (*sitting on floor near fireplace*). They shot me—and got my gun.

JANE. He's had a bad fever from the wound. He's terribly weak.

FATHER (*arrested in action of removing belt*). Well, that makes this cartridge belt useless. (*Throws it on table L.*) I couldn't get any more bullets for the pistols, but I've a few left. How many rounds left for the shotgun?

MOTHER. Three now.

FATHER. I brought some shells for it, but I lost them. (*He looks down at his buckskins.*)

ROBBIN (*fascinated, picking up the headdress* FATHER *flung off on entering*). Papa, where did you get the Indian clothes?

FATHER. I borrowed them, son.

ROBBIN. Borrowed them?

FATHER. There was an Indian scout out there by a tree—

ROBBIN. And you stalked him?

FATHER. I needed his clothes.

ROBBIN. So the other Indians would think you were one of them?

EMMA. And you could come in without their suspecting you.

JOE. Your papa knows some Indian tricks, eh, Robbin? (ROBBIN *hops back to small window UR, vigilant again as are the others.*)

FATHER (*looking around*). Molly, are you all safe? Where's Tommy?

MOTHER. Then he didn't get there!

EMMA. We sent him for you, Papa.

FATHER. When? When did he leave?

MOTHER. What time was it, Jane?

JANE. It was after midnight, I'm sure.

MOTHER. And he didn't get to the fort— What time did you leave?

FATHER. Before daylight. Work came along faster than we figured. I wanted to get you all back to the fort right away.

JOE (*looking out through crack*). It's getting light outside now.

MOTHER. Then—then you think he may—

FATHER. We'll just have to hope he got there.

JOE. But, if you didn't see Tommy, how did you know there was any trouble?

FATHER. Rover came along the Trail—headed for the fort— with a note on his collar.

MARY. Rover?

MOTHER. With a note?

FATHER. Yes.

JANE. Well, what—did it say?

JOE. Who wrote it?

FATHER. It was Tommy's writing.

MOTHER. Tommy's?

JANE. What did it say?

FATHER. Utahs—that's all I could make out. The paper was wet—

MOTHER. Oh, John! (*She almost breaks.*)

FATHER. Don't give up yet, Molly. Tommy may be all right.

JOE. Did Jacob get back?

FATHER. Yes, he returned last night.

JOE. Had he seen Wah-karrah?

ROBBIN. Had he found Kumo?

MARY. Papa, they tried to set the house afire!

EMMA. And they tried to pry the door open with a pitchfork!

JANE (*coming to* FATHER). Father!

FATHER. Well, Jane— It's been pretty rough, hasn't it?

JANE. Do you think Tommy is all right?

FATHER. Well— (*He and* MOTHER *look at each other.*)

JANE. You mean— (FATHER *shakes his head.* JANE *searches his face, then* MOTHER'S. *Then she starts to cry softly.* MARY *hides her face in* MOTHER'S *skirt.* ROBBIN *rubs his eyes.* EMMA *turns her head, takes handkerchief.*)

FATHER. Now, we mustn't give up hope. I have a feeling that Tommy is safe at the fort now.

JANE. Oh, do you? (*Others cheer up a bit.*)

JOE. Tommy probably got through all right.

EMMA. Then we ought to have help from the fort right away?

FATHER. Right away. (*Smiling reassuringly.*)

ROBBIN (*looking out window, UR*). Wow! Looks like we'll need it!

FATHER (*dashes to hole near door, R, to look out*). And right away!

MOTHER. What is it, John?

FATHER. About fifteen Indians!

ROBBIN. Papa, what have they got the big pole for?

FATHER (*ignoring the question, watching* INDIANS). Oh, if I had that rifle!

JOE. I'm sorry, sir.

FATHER. You couldn't help it, Joe. Only—when they get in range of these pistols and the shotgun, they're too close to see well out of these chinks.

ROBBIN. Papa, what have they got the big pole for?

FATHER. For a battering ram.

EMMA. They'll batter down the door!

ROBBIN. Guns!

EMMA. Every one of them!

JOE. The slavers trade them guns for papooses!

FATHER. They're coming! They're going to try to ram the door.

JANE. Ram it?

FATHER (*dividing out the ammunition, trying to keep cool and prevent panic*). Now, Mother, take my pistol. Here're five bullets. Joe, take yours. Here're five more. That's all, so take good aim. There's nothing much we can do to stop them.

JOE. Not against all those guns!

FATHER. But when they break through, let's give them all we've got. Robbin, Mary, you watch the windows. Emma, you stand in the bedroom door, and watch the shutters there. (*They all get ready.*) Now, every man to his post, and keep down. (*Outside begins a fitful barrage of gunfire, seemingly to cover the* INDIANS *battering the door. There is a thud outside, then a bang on the door.*)

JOE. Fifteen tall Injuns on a battering ram! Look out! They're coming in! (*The banging continues in a rhythmical pattern; sound of cracking boards.*)

FATHER. There goes the door.

JOE (*as the cupboard starts to move*). Now the cupboard.

MOTHER. I can see them through the crack in the door, John. (FATHER *moves to look. Takes aim. Fires.*)

JOE. Got the first one.

FATHER. Keep down! (*There are shots from outside.*)

JOE. Now give 'em the other barrel. (*As* FATHER *tries to aim.*) Look, there's one aiming at you. (FATHER *lets go with the*

*other barrel.) That fixed him! (More shots from the out-
side. Battering resumes, hardly interrupted. It is moving
the cupboard.)*

MOTHER *(looking out, suddenly pulls* FATHER *down).* John!
(There is a shot close by as he ducks.)

FATHER *(loading shotgun).* Only one shell left! I'll have to
save that till the last.

JOE. Look out. They're aiming! *(Just then there is the growing sound of horses approaching rapidly.)*

FATHER. Duck. *(He is crouched, ready to shoot.)*

JOE. Why don't they shoot? They've turned the other way!

JANE. Sounds like horses coming. *(Sound increasing.)*

ROBBIN. Oh, look! Another band of Indians!

MARY. On horses.

JOE. Then we're in for it. *(Shooting begins again outside.
Grows louder.)*

JANE. Oh, Papa, what shall we do now?

MOTHER. Just stand ready, Jane.

ROBBIN They're coming! *(He jumps down from cellar door
and runs over L by table, pointing to cellar. All but
FATHER, who is ready to fire out, turn to look.)*

TOMMY *(as cellar door lifts, appears in* KUMO's *tunic).* Father,
don't shoot!

MOTHER. Tommy!

FATHER. Son!

ALL. Tommy!

TOMMY. Those aren't Indians. They're the milita!

FATHER. The militia?

TOMMY. Yes. Jacob sent me in to tell you not to shoot them.

ROBBIN *(back at small window).* Sure! I can see Jacob and
Lyman Howd. *(*FATHER *shoves the cupboard upstage away
from the door.)*

MARY (*opening window L*). There's Jacob! (*Shooting sounds recede.*)

EMMA (*with* MARY *at window*). Tommy—Robbin, look! They've brought your pinto pony!

ROBBIN. Look, the Indians are running away!

EMMA. The militia are chasing them! (FATHER *throws open the door.*)

MOTHER (*running to* TOMMY). Oh, Tommy, Tommy!

TOMMY. Mother!

JANE. Tommy, Tommy, darling!

MARY (*running to* TOMMY, *throwing her arms around him*). Tommy! You brought the militia! (*They have all gathered around* TOMMY *near the fireplace, and* FATHER's *back is turned toward the door, when* WAN-TAH *rushes in, pursued by* HOWD *and* JACOB. JANE *sees him and screams. The family huddle by the mantel.* WAN-TAH *dashes toward the inner door, but a growl from* ROVER *stops him. As he turns back, uncertain,* HOWD *appears in doorway R, gun covering him.*)

HOWD (*to* WAN-TAH). Meah-bike-way! (FATHER, *grabbing* WAN-TAH's *tomahawk, taken in Act One, quickly edges between* WAN-TAH *and the door L as* JACOB *enters.*)

MOTHER (*softly*). Jacob!

HOWD. We had him surrounded. There was no place else for him to hide.

JACOB (*to* WAN-TAH, *quietly*). I have smoked the peace pipe, Wan-tah, with your brother chief. Wah-karrah says you are a traitor, a murderer and a thief. (*Watching* WAN-TAH's *crafty eyes and twitching muscles.*) Meah-bike-way! (*This is said quietly, but powerfully, to forestall any desperate attempt at escape or vengeance.*) We will take you to face Wah-karrah. (To HOWD, as he glances over shoulder out of door.) Our men are ready outside. (At his nod, HOWD and FATHER move in to force WAN-TAH outside. Just then POONE-KAATS, the papoose, appears in the doorway R. She looks from one to the other, frightened.)

POONE-KAATS. Kumo?

JACOB (to HOWD). Wait. (To WAN-TAH.) First tell Jacob what you have done with the Pah-Ute papoose. (WAN-TAH, arms folded, looks fierce defiance.) Well? (Eloquently, WAN-TAH gestures scalping. MARY, with a cry, runs to her mother. MOTHER looks horrified, the children sorrowful; men set their jaws. JACOB gestures to take him out.) Wah-karrah will punish you. (POONE-KAATS runs to get behind MOTHER. Just as WAN-TAH reaches the door, KUMO appears in the window. Taking in the situation, he lets out his wolf howl. All turn to him, even WAN-TAH. HOWD, with a grunt of disgust, shoves WAN-TAH outside. KUMO, standing in the window, still dressed as TOMMY, whips out the stolen mirror from his pouch and regards himself foolishly in it.)

POONE-KAATS (rushing to him). Kumo!

TOMMY. Kumo!

ALL. Kumo! (They rally round the INDIAN BOY.)

CURTAIN

GLOSSARY OF INDIAN WORDS

The author has sometimes extended the meanings of these words to fit situations in the play.

AT-AM-BAR	*Talk*
COO-NAH	*Fire*
CO-QUE	*Shoot*
E-IQUEAY	*Die (here used for Dead, which is E-I)*
HOL-LA	*Indian's attempt at Hello*
HUM-PAH	*What (here it means What is it?)*
IN-NE-TO-AH	*Get away*
ISH-UMP	*You lie. You have forked tongue.*
KATZ-KAR-RA	*Gone away*
KATZ-OATS	*Hat*
KUMO	*Jack rabbit (Pah-Ute)*
MAH-BE-NUNK	*To fly (here, Run)*
MEAH-BIKE-WAY	*Move, or move away (here, Don't move, also)*
MIKE-TICKABOO	*Greeting, salutation (usually friendly)*
MI-POODG-E	*Small (here, Coward)*
MUG-GI	*Give. Give to me.*
MUMP-I	*Exclamation of surprise (Pah-Ute)*
NAN-KUH-BAH	*Ear (here, Listen)*
NAN-ZITCH	*Girl*
NAU-VOO-NUMP	*Looking glass*
NE-AB	*Chief*
PA-POOSE	*Baby, child, small person*
PAH-UTE	*Ute living by the water (one division of the Utes)*
PAT-SUN	*Daughter (Pah-Ute)*
PE-ATS	*Mother*

PE-MO	Pants (here used to designate clothes)
PESHADNY	Speak or say
PIEK-A	Come (here, Come here)
PI-QUEAY	Go away (sometimes spelled Pi-queah)
POON-E-KEE	Look, see
POON-NY	Look (or POON-NY WON-Y, Look, stand)
POONE-KAATS	Poone—Skunk; Kaats—Packrat (here, name of girl)
POO-SUDS-WAY-AH	Understand. I understand. You understand.
PROWA	Indian attempt to say Flour
PUN-KER-RO	Go, go quickly (here, sometimes, Hurry)
SHIN-NOB	Devil (in Pah-Ute, refers to Younger God, brother of To-bats)
TAMMY-NAH-WAH	Come with me
TANG-I	Kick (here, Fight, also)
TO-PEECH-EE	Tie, tie up
TICK-A-BOO	Friend. (I am friend. You are friend, etc.)
TICK-I	Eat
TO-BUCK	Angry (here, mood of anger)
TO-WITCH-EE	Very much (here, used with Tick-a boo)
TSAP-KAK	Open the door
TUM-BY-O	Gun
TU-SHU-KRNT	Flour
UM-PI-O	Not certain
U-TAH	Probably, Tall Indian (a tribe or Indian of that tribe, a Ute)
VA-MOOSE	Go, vanish, get out (probably borrowed from Mexicans)

WAH-PANNA-KARRA *Gold*
WICKIUP *Indian dome-shaped dwelling*
YACK or YENNO *Hand to me*

Most of the words in the foregoing list are Ute (Utah); a few are Pah-Ute. An important thing to remember is that the Indians did not run their sounds together, but separated syllables quite distinctly. They articulated their words precisely. For example, while the name of one tribe is spelled Piute or Paiute, following our English pronunciation of it, the Indian said Pah-Ute, without using any glide.

PRODUCTION NOTES

The dog can be trained as well as any other "actor" and adds much to the enjoyment of players and audience. If necessary, he can be managed with a black string leash. The scenes are arranged so that if he is gun-shy, he may be kept outside during the firing.

Log cabin set: The trap door is provided by the box-like bench seat with lid or door opening into the cellar below. To enter from the outside, an opening is left in the flat back of the box. The right end of the box can be left open (near the wall and masked by the cupboard) so that the papoose can slip into the box when Mother is attacked by Wan-tah. The audience will watch Father and Wan-tah, while Mother can move near the open end for the papoose to get out from under her skirts. The audience will not know the papoose is in the box or how she got there. If necessary, the lid of the box can be in two sections so that the papoose can lift it more easily to come out.

The openings necessary to spread the action when the family watch the outside can be chink holes with the fillers removed for the purpose, or can be porthole-like openings. There should be one in the wall R downstage of the cupboard and one over the table in the left wall, at least. The look-out window above the cellar door and ordinary cracks provide other places for seeing out.

The great amount of action in this set can be suggested. When the pitchfork comes through the crack of the door, care must be taken to see that the set is not shaken. It is easy to give the appearance of energetic action and still not break the illusion by shaking the set. When Father hammers the nails in the door, this can be done, if necessary, after the cupboard is moved in place, Father faking the hammering above the cupboard with the sound provided offstage. When the door is being rammed, the thuds can be done on the stage floor off.

The smoke required can be made with a smudge pot, dry ice, or with ingredients any chemist can suggest. Little water need be used in putting out the fire. With care, most of the action can be masked. For buttermilk, use ordinary scene whiting.

Forest set: The rocks can be constructed of boxes built out with chicken wire, covered with canvas or burlap and painted.

STAGE PROPERTIES

ACT ONE

       Fireplace unit, andirons, tripod, kettle
          On mantel: 2 large candles in rough holders
            Mexican vases, basket
       Chest
       High, old-fashioned cupboard with doors
          Cookie jar
          Calendar
       Rough table, 2 benches
       Rocking chair
       Woodbox with wood
       Water barrel with dipper
       Flour bin
       Stool
       Churn
       Small keg
       Rag rug
       On walls: Animal skin, deer head, Navajo rug
          Shelf and rack

ACT TWO

       Same

ACT THREE

     Scene One
       Large boulder
       2 smaller rocks
     Scene Two
       Same as ACT ONE

HAND PROPERTIES

ACT ONE

       Sunbonnet   JANE
       Mirror   "
       Shawl   "

Toy gun	TOMMY
Cartridge shell	"
Gold watch	"
Pencil	"
Swill bucket	"
Bow and arrow	KUMO
Butter mold	MOTHER
Rifle	JOE
Pistol	"
Wooden grub box	FATHER
Water bag	"
Bed roll	"
Shotgun	"
Knife	WAN-TAH
Tomahawk	"
Wood	ROBBIN, MARY
Bucket	"
Milk	EMMA
Jars	"

ACT TWO

Basin	JANE
Cloth	"
Candle	"
Pistol	TOMMY
Knife	"
Hat, coat, scarf	"
Tomahawk	"
Shawl	MOTHER
Shotgun	"
Buckets	"
Rag rug	"
Cloths	ROBBIN
Sacks	EMMA
Keg of buttermilk	"
Pitchfork	Offstage

ACT THREE
    Scene One

Watch	TOMMY
Shell (cartridge)	"
Pencil	"
Brown paper scrap	"
String	"
Thongs	WAN-TAH
Knife	"
Mirror	PIANG-KA

    Scene Two

Coat	MOTHER
Pail	"
Cartridge belt	FATHER
Bullets	"
Pistol	"
Tomahawk	"
Note in shell	ROBBIN
Hammer	"
Poker	EMMA
Nails	"
Pistol	JOE
Mirror	KUMO

COSTUMES   Period costumes can be made or rented, both for Indian and white characters. Guns can be rented reasonably or borrowed.

MUSIC   Music can be used effectively at opening and closing curtains during the play. If recorded music is not possible, drums can be used.

    At the close of the curtain in Act One, as the noise fades out, the savage rhythms of the *War Dance* (Cheyenne), RCA VICTOR 22144-A, could be faded in and up for about a minute. This could be repeated with fuller volume at close of Act Two. The *Shawnee Indian Hunt-*

ing Dance, RCA VICTOR 22144-B, has the appropriate mood for the opening and closing of the forest scene. Other useful records: MAJOR RECORDS #5033-A, *Indians* (1. Indian yells and war cries; 2. Indian war dance; 3. Indian feast dance) and the *Sioux and Navajo* album of the ETHNIC FOLKWAYS LIBRARY.

SOUND

Wagon wheels
Dog barks, yelps, growl
Wolf howls
Gunfire: pistol, shotgun
Rattling of shutters
Hammering
Thuds of battering ram
Wood cracking
Horses hoof beats

Papa Pompino
and the Prizefighter

A COMEDY-FANTASY IN MODERN DRESS

BY MARTHA BENNETT KING

EDITORS' NOTE

Papa Pompino and the Prizefighter is a rare play in that it treats a group of modern children in a believable way; uses fantasy with neither sentimentality nor tongue-in-cheek condescension; and achieves its excitement not through melodrama but from the conflicts resulting from the inner needs of the characters.

The theme of the play—the need to belong, to be accepted and understood—makes this an excellent vehicle for use on special occasions highlighting inter-group or international understanding, particularly since the theme, inherent in the dramatic structure of the play, is not expressed directly. The differences in race and national origin of the Bambinos (which could be altered to fit a local situation) are only implied and the point never labored.

The plot is clearly developed but care should be taken that the chases and fights do not reach such a pitch that their point in the plot is lost and that they become merely excitement for its own sake. The scene where Humpty, through the encouragement of others, puts himself together again and reaches the point where he can be accepted is the psychological climax of the play and should be given full value.

The most demanding part is that of Humpty. The boy who plays him must be able to establish the comic, over-protected side of his character, but also understand and project, from the beginning, Humpty's desire to be something else, thus arousing the audience's curiosity and eventual sympathy.

This play will lend itself well to arena staging or outdoor production. In conventional presentation it offers good opportunity for imaginative design.

PAPA POMPINO
AND THE PRIZEFIGHTER
A Comedy-Fantasy in Modern Dress

CHARACTERS

PAPA POMPINO, spry, pixie-like, of uncertain age. Once a clown in the circus, he has never lost the enchanted spirit of childhood.

H.M.T. DUMBTOP III, nicknamed HUMPTY. He is too fat, seems to lack muscular coordination and physical initiative. He is mentally very bright, however, and his difficulties are the result of his mother's fears.

BURLY BINKOWITZ, an ex-prizefighter, now HUMPTY's body-guard

JOHN

ERIC

FELIX

GUNDER

PAMELA

MARINA

TSING LING

WINNIE

THE BAMBINOS, a group of children who have formed a club which meets regularly on the hilltop with PAPA POMPINO

AGNES, a maid in the Dumbtop household

PLACE: The wall of a large estate

TIME: The present

ACT ONE: The wall at the back of the estate

Four in the afternoon

ACT TWO: *The same*

The following afternoon

ACT THREE: *The same*

Sundown

NOTE ON THE SETTINGS *

The action takes place on and around a stone wall which marks one boundary of a long-deserted estate. The stones of the wall contain quartz and sandstone which glow in rose and brown tones. An apple tree rises behind the wall, its branches forming a comfortable seat. There is a low thick bush stage L,† large enough to hide one person. There is a tree stage R, suggesting wooded land. A flagpole stands extreme R on the wall, Papa Pompino's pennant flying from it.

This single set may be very simply executed, using drapes or a cyclorama. As the play has a certain degree of fantasy, it would be in keeping with its style, as well as a means of simple production, to use two dimensional set pieces for the bush and tree and for the apple tree above the wall. In this case Papa Pompino would sleep on the wall itself rather than in the apple tree. However, if a more detailed, realistic and elaborate production is desired, it would not violate the style of the play.

The wall must be practical, as the characters climb on it, run along its top, and jump from it. The face of the wall may be flat, with the contours of the stones indicated by the painting.

ACT ONE

SCENE: *Across the back of the stage is a stone wall, an apple tree behind it. A large bush is stage L. A tree is stage R. A ladder is against the wall. It is about four in the afternoon.*

---

* Full production notes will be found at the end of the play.

† The following abbreviations are used throughout: C—center stage; R—right stage; L—left stage; U—upstage; D—downstage.

As the curtain opens, the stage is empty. PAPA POMPINO *looks over the wall from behind, disappears for a second, pops up, pulls himself halfway up, peers R and L, then climbs onto the wall. He takes an old-fashioned watch from his pocket, grins with pleasure as he finds he is early for an appointment. He sits down in the apple tree and consults his watch again, this time opening its back cover. He removes a small folded paper, smoothes it open, glances at it, refolds it and shakes his head as if baffled. He puts watch back in pocket while still holding the paper. Suddenly he looks up at the flagpole and scrambles to take his pennant down. As he goes, he puts the folded paper in the band of his hat. He returns to his seat in the tree, tucking the pennant into his pocket. Once more he looks R and L with an impish grin, then settles down for a cat nap. He begins to snore immediately and fails to hear voices and laughter off L.* PAMELA *and* TSING LING *run on. They stop abruptly as they see* PAPA POMPINO.

PAMELA. Sleeping again.

TSING LING. He didn't even hear us.

PAMELA. He never does unless we call his name. (*Shakes head in dismay.*) He's going to get in trouble some day, sleeping so hard. (*A shower of colored balls falls around the girls.* ERIC *and* JOHN *enter L.*)

JOHN. You can't catch a thing any more.

GIRLS. Sh . . . (*Pointing to* PAPA. *The* BOYS *groan.*)

ERIC. He hasn't even got his clown suit on. How's he going to practice with us?

PAMELA. Did you bring the trunk of costumes?

ERIC. Felix and Gunder are bringing it.

TSING LING. We still have to get the sandwiches, Pamela.

PAMELA. Shall we wake Papa first?

ERIC. Let's scare him. (*He pantomimes how they'll startle* PAPA *with war whoops. He walks to wall, reaches up pretending to pull* PAPA's *foot, motions to others to move away, then runs himself. As they go, they let out war whoops, patting their mouths with hands.* PAPA POMPINO *leaps to ground, looks around, tiptoes R as if expecting to catch someone. Returns running clown style, apparently getting nowhere, dives behind the bush, then crawls off L as* WINNIE *and* MARINA *enter R.*)

WINNIE (*calling*). Papa. Papa Pompino. I've brought Marina. She's going to join our club. (*Still ·calling without seeing anyone.*) She's going to dance in our show. Papa . . . Oh, dear, his flag isn't up.

MARINA. What flag?

WINNIE. His coat of arms. He hangs it up when he's at home. Well, we'll just have to wait till he comes. (*She picks up a forgotten ball and begins to toss it from hand to hand, finally drops it and fails to pick it up.*)

MARINA. Where's his house?

WINNIE. He doesn't have one exactly. He mostly lives on this wall.

MARINA. Does he sleep here? (WINNIE *nods.*) Even in the rain?

WINNIE. Oh, he has a little tent. He brought it from the circus, but it's full of holes and lets all the rain in anyway. (*Seriously.*) That's why we're going to give a show. All the Bambinos are going to sell tickets and we're going to build a shack house for Papa. Only you musn't tell. Promise?

MARINA. Promise. (*Crosses her heart.*) But you said Papa was going to be in the show.

WINNIE. He is. Only he doesn't know why we're going to sell tickets.

MARINA. Where will you put his house?

WINNIE. Right here. Papa wouldn't ever go away from the wall. It's his castle, he says. (*Mimicking* PAPA.) "I'm a rich man. Here is my castle (*makes sweeping gestures*) and you are all my Bambinos."

MARINA (*dreamily*). Bambinos means children, doesn't it?

WINNIE. "My children and my friends."

MARINA. Winnie, what if somebody should move into the big house? (*Pointing off.*)

WINNIE. Oh, they won't. Nobody's lived in that house for years and years.

MARINA. But if someone should buy the house and all these grounds . . . could Papa still live here?

WINNIE (*uneasy*). Nobody's going to move in. Not ever. We wouldn't let them.

MARINA (*changing subject*). Winnie, when will I really be a Bambino?

WINNIE. Just as soon as Papa performs the ceremony. Let's go for your costume now. (*They exit R as* FELIX *enters L and* GUNDER *appears over the wall.*)

FELIX. Hey, I've been looking for you. You're supposed to help carry the trunk.

GUNDER (*gloomily*). There isn't going to be any show.

FELIX. Why not?

GUNDER. Somebody's moving into the big house.

FELIX (*horrified*). How do you know?

GUNDER. Man in the post office said so.

FELIX. Who?

GUNDER. I've never seen him before.

FELIX. Then it isn't true. (*Talking to reassure himself.*) Nobody's lived there for a hundred years. Not since I was born. (*They are each lost in thought.*) If anybody did move in, the club wouldn't have a place to meet.

GUNDER (*nodding grim assent*). And what about Papa Pompino?

FELIX. Say, we really have to give our show now. We gotta make a whole carload of money. Listen, Gunder. Don't tell anybody else. They'd all get excited and wouldn't practice.

GUNDER. Yeah. Besides if anybody does move in it won't be for days. We'll give our show and have enough money to buy Papa a new home before anybody knows what we're doing. Let's get the trunk. (*They exit L.* PAPA *runs on from R as if hotly pursued, wipes brow with huge handkerchief, leans on wall to catch his breath, fails to hear anyone coming, picks up ladder, places it against wall and climbs up slowly. Grinning, he points in various directions, counting to eight on his fingers as if he knew just where each Bambino was. Sits down, starts to fan self with his hat, sees folded paper stuck in hat band, takes it out with a frown which implies he ought to be more careful, opens his watch and puts paper inside back cover. Relaxes in tree as if he were going to fall asleep. Snores once.* HUMPTY *calls off R.*)

HUMPTY. Burly. (PAPA *snores.*) Burly. (PAPA *wakes self with a jerk.*) Burly. (*The voice is nearer.* PAPA *almost falls behind the wall as* BURLY *strides on.* PAPA *looks cautiously over wall at* BURLY *who is holding his head as if it were going to burst.* HUMPTY *comes puffing on.*) Burly, you're supposed to wait for me. (BURLY *throws up his hands in despair.*)

BURLY. Trapped. Me. Burly Binkowitz.

HUMPTY. Stay right here. I want to explore.

BURLY. Okay. Okay. (*Slumps down on ground and leans against wall, head in hands.*)

HUMPTY (*looking around eagerly*). Is this all my new property?

BURLY. Your old man bought the whole hill.

HUMPTY. Then this is my wall, too. (*He looks at it a moment, then turns his back as* PAPA *looks over in openmouthed amazement. Pantomimes his speechless protest. Takes piece of folded paper from watch and waves it as evidence that the wall is his. Pats the wall, puts the folded paper in one pocket, watch in the other, and disappears angrily.* HUMPTY *turns and moves to ladder, puts a foot on lowest rung in a gingerly fashion.* BURLY *looks up and springs to his feet.*)

BURLY. Hey you, no climbing.

HUMPTY (*stepping to ground without protest*). I wasn't climbing. But I could if I wanted to.

BURLY (*with disgust*). Sure.

HUMPTY. I could run up that ladder if I wanted to.

BURLY. If you could even walk up, you wouldn't need a bodyguard like me. Golly, I have to take care of you like you was a crate of eggs.

HUMPTY (*justifying himself*). Mother says I inherited very brittle bones. (*He puts his hand on the ladder with no intention to climb.* BURLY *grabs the ladder and puts it on the ground beside the wall.*) My grandfather had very brittle bones, too. His bones would break just like that. (*Claps hands.*)

BURLY (*as if repeating an old story*). And all the king's horses and all the king's men couldn't put him together again.

HUMPTY (*as if the family had been maligned*). It's true. (*He spies a colored ball and picks it up.* BURLY *takes it from him.*)

BURLY. Where did that come from?

HUMPTY (*excited*). Some boys threw it.

BURLY. There aren't any boys around here.

HUMPTY (*obviously given to flights of imagination and wishful thinking*). Yes, there are. They come right up over this hill every day.

BURLY (*very suspicious*). How do you know that?

HUMPTY. I've been studying the situation. I have a map. The town is over that way. (*He points off R.*) But there are factories and a lot of houses down that way (*L*). The river is over there, too. The children who live down there (*L*) come up over this hill every day in order to get to school down there (*R*). It's much too far around by the road.

BURLY (*grimly*). Well, I'll fix them.

HUMPTY (*lost in his dream*). I'll see them when they come.

BURLY (*alarmed*). Hey, you heard your old man. No mingling with the hoi poloi.

HUMPTY (*still lost*). I could even play with them.

BURLY. Just let me catch any kids loafing around here. No sir. No kids going to bring a lot of measles and chicken pox around this prize ring. (*He begins to punch out like a fighter.* PAPA *looks over the wall again, startled.* HUMPTY *gets back to reality and watches* BURLY *admiringly.*)

HUMPTY. You were the best prizefighter in the whole world, weren't you, Burly?

BURLY. Kayo Champ of the world. (PAPA *claps hand to head and disappears.*)

HUMPTY. Show me how you knocked everybody out.

BURLY (*pretending modesty*). Aw, it wasn't anything. (*Begins to demonstrate.*) I just walked out in the ring kind of slow and sized the guy up. Then I'd get going. (*Pantomimes a fight, dancing, feinting, swinging, punching.*) Sometimes it took a few rounds, but when I got ready, down he'd go . . . out for the count. . . . One, two, three . . .

HUMPTY (*excited, imitating clumsily*). That's good. That's good. He comes up and you knock him out. Bang. Biff. (BURLY *is surprised, catches* HUMPTY's *arm.*)

BURLY. Hey, take it easy. You heard your old man. No fighting.

HUMPTY (*relaxing*). Why did you have to stop fighting?

BURLY (*not pleased at the memory*). Cracked my skull. Couldn't do anything without getting dizzy. (*Realizes he's running himself down.*) But I can still fight. Nobody pulls any monkey business around Binkowitz. Come on. We're getting out of here. (*He strides off* L. HUMPTY *starts, but pauses as he hears voices off* R.)

VOICES (*calling*). Papa. Papa Pompino. (PAPA *looks fearfully over the wall. He fails to see* HUMPTY, *who stands close to wall.* PAPA *signals with handkerchief, hoping to keep children back, then drops behind wall.* BURLY *returns.*)

BURLY. What you waiting for?

HUMPTY (*thinking fast*). I have something in my shoe. I can't walk. (BURLY *gets down on one knee in disgust, takes shoe off and shakes it.* HUMPTY *is watching off.*)

BURLY (*almost choking with frustration*). Me. Burly Binkowitz in training to be a nursemaid. (AGNES *enters* L.)

AGNES. Thank goodness I found you.

BURLY (*angry at being caught in present role*). Okay. What do you want?

AGNES (*angry in turn, pretends great elegance*). I don't want anything, Mr. Binkowitz. Mr. Dumbtop wants you . . . on the telephone.

BURLY (*flustered*). Hey. Maybe he wants me in New York. (*Starts off.*)

HUMPTY. Wait for me.

BURLY. Golly, no. I gotta run. You'd fall down and bust something sure. (*Starts off in a frenzy, but returns, grabs* HUMPTY's *shoulders and presses down as if to anchor him to the spot.*) Look. You stand right there till I get back. (*Grabs* AGNES *and presses her down.*) You stay right with him. (*Starts off again, pauses, takes a police whistle from his pocket and gives it to* AGNES.) Here. If you need anything, blow. (*Exit L.*)

AGNES. Well, who does he think he is? I've got my own job to do. Come on. (*She takes* HUMPTY *by the arm as if to go home but he stands firm.*)

HUMPTY. Burly said to stay here.

AGNES. He didn't know what he was saying. Come along. Your mother will be all upset if I don't finish pressing her things.

HUMPTY (*inspired by desire to see who called offstage*). Agnes, you can go home alone.

AGNES (*almost wailing*). I'm not supposed to leave you.

HUMPTY. Give me the whistle. I'll blow if I need anything.

AGNES. Oh, what shall I do?

HUMPTY. Go home. Mother will be all upset. (*Holds out hand and she gives him whistle.*) Now tell Burly I want him to hurry back. (AGNES *goes off L.*)

VOICES (*calling far off*). Papa! Papa Pompino. (*Voices pick up the call in other directions.* HUMPTY *hides behind the bush.* PAPA *appears cautiously, surprised at finding no one, listens with worried expression to the* BAMBINOS' *calls, de-*

cides not to worry them, leaps to wall and fastens his pennant to the flagpole. Grins, falls into the spirit of hide-and-seek and ducks out of sight as JOHN and ERIC enter L with a picnic hamper which they place beside the tree R. PAMELA and TSING LING follow.)

JOHN. Boy, that's going to be a real feast.

PAMELA. Flag's up. He's here. (A shower of colored balls comes over the wall. All scramble to get them.)

ERIC. Ten points to the one who catches Papa. (They race off in different directions. WINNIE and MARINA enter. The pandemonium of the offstage chase builds up in the following scene.)

WINNIE. They're playing the game already. You're supposed to catch Papa. (MARINA puts her costume by the tree and the two dart off. HUMPTY steps out of the bush to watch. He ducks back as PAPA runs on. PAPA pauses to catch his breath. He puts his hand in his pocket and discovers the piece of folded paper. Exasperated at his own carelessness, he carefully takes out his watch and puts the paper back, places watch in pocket. His back is toward the bush and HUMPTY can't see what he's doing though he cranes his neck. PAPA darts off as ERIC runs on, whistles loudly and scrambles over the wall. HUMPTY is very excited, stands up and blows his police whistle. FELIX and GUNDER enter with costume trunk. It's heavy and they drop it near the tree, listening.)

GUNDER. Who's got a whistle like that?

FELIX. Sounded like a police whistle. Maybe Eric has one.

GUNDER. I don't feel much like playing the game, do you?

FELIX. No. I gotta funny feeling in here. (Touches his stomach.)

GUNDER. I feel like a disaster was hanging around.

FELIX. Anyway, we have to pretend we feel good. Let's stop everybody and practice.

GUNDER. Did you bring the tickets to sell?

FELIX. Hundred and sixty.

GUNDER (startled). We can't sell a hundred and sixty in sixty million years.

FELIX. Yes, we can! There are eight Bambinos. If we only sell twenty tickets each, it's a hundred and sixty.

GUNDER. Fifteen cents each. How much money will we have if we do sell them? (They pause for mental arithmetic, but a high voice squeaks from the bushes.)

HUMPTY (unseen). Twenty-four dollars.

GUNDER (thinking it a trick). Papa! Get him. (The two dart off. Shouts are heard on all sides. HUMPTY steps out and calls feebly. Hides as the BAMBINOS return from all sides.)

ERIC. What's the matter with us today? I haven't even had a glimpse of Papa.

WINNIE. Well, I wish somebody would find him. I'm tired.

TSING LING. I can't run another step. I have a stitch in my side.

PAMELA. Me, too. Let's try coaxing him to come out.

GUNDER. Eric's good at that. Go on, Eric.

FELIX. Listen, everybody. When Papa comes he has to perform the ceremony for Marina. (ALL ad lib. their approval.) Then let's serve Papa the finest feast he's ever had.

PAMELA. We only brought sandwiches.

FELIX. We'll pretend. It's important for Papa to be very happy today.

WINNIE. What's special about today . . . except Marina.

GUNDER. You'll find out soon enough. Put on your costumes while Eric calls Papa. (They open the trunk. ERIC takes out a jester's cap and bells, puts it on and begins to parade

on the wall, calling "Papa," while the others dress up.
FELIX *wears robe and crown of a king.* WINNIE *becomes the
Queen of Hearts.* JOHN *is the Knave of Hearts.* MARINA
puts on a gypsy skirt and carries a tambourine. TSING LING
dons a Chinese robe. GUNDER *has a guard's helmet and
spear and* PAMELA *wears a peaked hat with a flowing veil.*)

ERIC (*parading on wall*). Come out, Papa Pompino. We re-
fuse to hunt for you any more. We're now putting on
costumes for our show. Hear me, Papa? Hear me? (ERIC
*continues jingling his bells and executing fancy dance
steps.*) I make sweeter music than birds in the trees. I sail
through the air with the greatest of ease. (*Leaps to ground.*)
I roll (*turns somersault*) like a snail. I spout (*spouts*) like
a whale. I carry your troubles away . . . (JOHN *interrupts,
handing him a bucket with a low bow, at the same time
finishing his rhyme—*)

JOHN. In a pail. Here, sir. I give you a bucket to carry your
foul poetry away. (ERIC *throws pail back at him.* FELIX *has
mounted the wall. He claps his hands loudly.*)

FELIX. Jester, where is the rogue, Pompino?

ERIC (*bowing*). The rogue has vanished, O King. He has fallen
beneath the oak leaves and lies sleeping.

FELIX. Bring him to me at once or off with your heads.

TSING LING (*fluttering*). Come out, Papa Pompino, I don't
wish to lose my head. (JOHN *motions everyone to silence.*)
I know what will get him. (GUNDER *has helped the* QUEEN
OF HEARTS *to climb the ladder in dainty style and sit by
the* KING.)

JOHN. Queen, will you serve us all tarts? (*Pretends to hand
them up.*) Or must I steal them once more?

WINNIE. I'll serve you all tarts. King, which will you have?
Apple, cherry, chocolate, peach?

FELIX. Hm . . . (*Looking them over.*) Peach.

JOHN. Cherry for mine. (*Others ad lib. their choices and pretend to eat.*) Never have I tasted such tarts. (*Others agree with elaborate praise.*) Deluptuous. Delectable. Delunchable. Um . . . (PAPA *looks over the wall. All exclaim in relief.*)

PAPA. Did someone say tarts? (*He scrambles up on the wall and* WINNIE *pretends to pass him the tarts.* PAPA *accepts one in the same spirit. Then leaps to the ground.* FELIX *follows, then turns to assist the* QUEEN.)

WINNIE (*calling before she gets down*). Papa. You must perform the ceremony. Marina must be a Bambino. (GUNDER *carries the ladder off L.*)

PAPA. Delighted. Delighted. Never too many Bambinos. Where is my sword? (*He takes a sword offered by* ERIC.) Kneel down, Miss Marina. (*She kneels and* PAPA *lays the sword on her shoulder.*) Do you promise to be a true and helpful friend in all kinds of weather?

MARINA. I do.

PAPA. Will you be kind to all people, young and old, rich and poor, black, white or yellow?

MARINA. I will.

PAPA. Then rise, good Marina. With this sword of faith I have made you one of our band, a Bambino. (MARINA *rises.* ALL *cheer.* WINNIE *throws her arms around* MARINA. PAPA *leaps into the air, crosses his feet and sits down in one elegant motion. He holds a hand out to* MARINA *to have her sit beside him.*) Now for the feast. (*The* CHILDREN *begin a comic-fantasy, their movements and words weaving into a rhythmic dance pattern. Momentarily each holds the center of attention as he pretends to serve* PAPA *and* MARINA, *holding out platters and trays and bowls.* ERIC *first pretends to tie a napkin around* PAPA's *neck. The girls pretend to walk with trays on their heads.*) Music. I would have music for the feast. (ALL *hum softly.*) Wind, play on your harps. Snails, rattle your shells. Ripple, you waters. (ALL *pantomime his orders.*)

GUNDER (*bowing and offering great tray*).

> I start the feast, good Papa Pompino,
> With Smörgåsbord, the pride of Sweden,
> Broiled fresh herring and good red salmon,
> Scarlet shrimp and pickled onion.

(PAPA *examines the tray with delight, reaches into the picnic hamper which has been moved near him and takes out a sandwich to munch. He waves it in thanks to* GUNDER.)

PAPA. Skoal. (PAMELA *steps in with her tray, moving it so that* PAPA *can catch all its fragrance.*)

PAMELA. Smell, Papa Pompino. When my grandmother came to this country she was so very poor, she brought only her cooking pot and her head full of memories. When she cooks in the pot, it is magic. The odors rise and drift through the windows and all of the neighbors come running.

PAPA. Wonderful. Scrumdumptuous . . . delectable.

TSING LING. Please, Papa Pompino. Eggs that are scrambled? And Bird's Nest Soup?

PAPA. Ah, something I have not tasted before.

ERIC. For you, Papa, chicken paprika. (*The tempo picks up and moves faster and faster so that the entire scene takes little time.*)

FELIX. Sweet potatoes stuffed with prunes.

PAPA. Oh, my. (*Loosening belt.*)

JOHN. Sire, I would offer you Irish stew but I fear for your capacity.

PAPA. Away, low jester. (JOHN *cartwheels or somersaults away.*)

WINNIE. Pancakes, Papa Pompino. Little thin pancakes with maple syrup and melted butter.

PAPA. Hold. No more. I am unable to take another mouthful.

GUNDER. Then we are ready to practice our show.

PAMELA (*sternly*). Papa, where is your clown suit?

PAPA (*scurrying off stage, still eating a sandwich*). One moment. Don't wait.

ALL. Hurry. Hurry.

HUMPTY (*in his excitement has forgotten to hide and has become one of the group in imagination*). Hurry. (CHILDREN *are speechless with surprise.* HUMPTY *realizes what he has done and desperately retreats.* FELIX *and* JOHN *grab him and keep him C.*)

JOHN. How did you get here?

FELIX. Who are you?

HUMPTY (*thoroughly frightened, calls out*). Burly! Help. (*Voice is high and squeaky.*)

PAMELA. You don't need to yell for help. Just tell us who you are.

HUMPTY. Burly, Burly.

JOHN. Come on. Tell us your name.

HUMPTY. Burly.

FELIX. Wait a minute. (*Turns to* GUNDER.) I've got an idea who he is. (*Turns to* HUMPTY.) Where do you live?

HUMPTY. Burly. (BURLY *rushes on. The boys release* HUMPTY's *arms and he falls backwards.* BURLY *catches him and tries to take the situation in. He gets on his knees beside* HUMPTY, *who has slumped down completely.*)

BURLY. What goes on here, anyway. Are you hurt, Kid? Why didn't you blow the whistle? (*He feels* HUMPTY's *arms and* legs. *Props him to a sitting position, then suddenly lets him fall flat as he stands up to face the astonished group of children.*) Get out of here. Don't you know this is private property?

PAMELA. It's our property. This is where we always play.

BURLY. This is H.M.T. Dumbtop's property.

WINNIE. How could it be?

BURLY. He lives here.

PAMELA. Where does he live?

BURLY. In the big house. Where do you think?

JOHN. Nobody's lived in that house for years.

BURLY. Well, somebody lives there now.

WINNIE. They couldn't. They just couldn't.

BURLY (*exasperated*). Look. I'm telling you. H.M.T. Dumbtop lives there.

HUMPTY (*high voice, wishing to be friendly as he looks on from behind* BURLY). I'm H.M.T. Dumbtop, the third.

BURLY. Yeah. And you've busted his bones.

JOHN. We didn't do a thing to him.

BURLY. How do I know? (*Puts arm around* HUMPTY, *who is still sitting on ground.*) I'll get you to a doctor right away, Kid (*turns to group*), and you get out of here. And don't let me ever see you again.

PAMELA. You have no right to order us around.

BURLY. Get this. I'm Burly Binkowitz, bodyguard to young Dumbtop, and I got orders to keep kids out of the place. So I'm going to.

HUMPTY. He's a very good prizefighter, too.

BURLY. Come on, Kid. (BURLY *half carries* HUMPTY *off L, leaving the children angry and bewildered.*)

JOHN. A prizefighter.

PAMELA. He's the worst person I've ever seen.

ERIC. Bodyguard to that little brat. How do you like that?

FELIX (*mimicking* HUMPTY's *high voice*). You're speaking of H.M.T. Dumbtop, the third.

WINNIE. Old Humpty Dumpty Dumbtop. That's what he is. And he's spoiled everything. (*She begins to take off her costume.*)

TSING LING. Don't cry, Winnie. Papa will think of something.

MARINA (*appalled*). What will happen to Papa? (*They all stop and stare.*)

GUNDER. We'll have to find a new home for him.

TSING LING. Maybe he can go back to the circus.

ERIC. He's too old. He can't go on being a clown forever. (PAPA *bounces onto the wall wearing his clown suit, big shoes, bulbous nose, funny hat and all. He carries a folded umbrella.*)

PAPA. Howdy . . . howdy . . . howdy . . . (*Shakes hands with himself.*) Ladeez and gents, you are about to witness the greatest parachute jump in history. (*He opens his big umbrella and points upward.*) Watch the daredevil Pompino come hurtling out of the skies. He's jumped. He's coming down . . . a mere speck in the sky. Watch closely. He's closer . . . closer . . . closer . . . Watch him come. Keep your eyes glued to the master jumper. Here he comes. Look out below. Look out. (*He makes a crazy jump as he ends his spiel on a high note.*) Say, what's the matter with everybody? (*The children are standing expressionless.*) Where's the wild applause?

WINNIE (*flinging her arms around* PAPA). Oh, Papa. (PAPA *pushes her gently aside and starts a series of clown routines, talking to himself as he performs. The group does not enter into his game.*)

PAPA. Dear me. Dear me. Must be a thundercloud around

someplace. See all the gloomy faces. (*He peers into first one face after another.*) Never seen an audience like it. The great Pompino can't make a single one laugh.

PAMELA. You might as well stop, Papa. Something terrible has happened.

PAPA (*pretending not to understand*). Whoops. (*He falls over his shoes and rolls.*) Something terrible, terrible, terrible. (*Gets back on his feet and grins.*) Well, not too terrible. I'll wager it can be fixed.

GUNDER (*taking* PAPA's *arm*). You better sit down and listen, Papa.

PAPA (*drawing back*). If the news is bad, I'll take it standing up.

FELIX. Papa, we have to get out of here.

WINNIE. We can't give our show or anything. (*She picks up costumes which have been dropped and puts them in the trunk.*)

PAPA. Who's been telling you such pretty stories?

JOHN. That prizefighter.

FELIX. It's really Dumbtop, the one who owns the place.

PAPA (*he knows the answers but wants the group to talk*). What place?

FELIX. The house, Papa. The big house.

GUNDER. Man named H.M.T. Dumbtop's moved in.

ERIC. Yeah, this is private property now.

PAMELA. Don't worry, Papa. We'll find you a place to live.

GUNDER (*solemnly*). Papa Pompino, you can live with us. My mother and father will be very happy to have you live with us.

FELIX. You can live with us, too.

PAPA. Thank you, my friends. Thank you. But I enjoy life immensely right here on this wall. Fresh air. Stars above

me when I sleep. I am a rich man. This is my castle, and
you are all my Bambinos.

WINNIE. Poor Papa.

JOHN. You better get your things and come with us now.
(ALL ad lib.)

PAPA. My gracious me. What's come over you? I haven't the
slightest intention of leaving my home. (BURLY *looks over
wall from behind. The group sees him.* ALL *shout.*)

ALL. Look out. Run, Papa. (PAPA *turns, skips nimbly aside
as* BURLY *hurdles over the wall. They face each other, each
with feet spread apart.*)

BURLY. So, now we got a clown.

PAPA (*bowing*). At your service, sir.

BURLY. Don't sir me. I told these kids to get out of here and
I meant it. Get going—you and your ragamuffins.

PAPA. Sir, it is you who must get going. (*Jumps at* BURLY.)
Get out. (BURLY *is startled and steps back.* PAPA *steps up
and pushes his great nose right into* BURLY'S *face.*) That's
right. Get out. (BURLY *gives* PAPA *a shove which nearly
upsets him.*) Just a minute, my good man. (PAPA *holds a
hand out like a policeman.*) You're standing on my
property.

BURLY (*hands on hips, jaw out*). This joint belongs to H.M.T.
Dumbtop.

PAPA (*calmly*). If you are referring to the gentleman who has
moved into that prison of rooms atop the hill, you may
give him my blessing. Also be good enough to inform him
that his property ends twenty feet the other side of the
wall. The wall and twenty feet on either side belong to
me. (HUMPTY *has crept back and is listening. The children
all begin to talk at once.*)

ALL (*ad lib.*). Papa, do you mean it? Is it really your property? Do you own it?

BURLY (*scratching his head*). I don't get it.

PAPA. Very simple, my friend. My Uncle Tony gave it to me.

HUMPTY. Can you prove it? (ALL *are surprised to see him.* BURLY *leaps to his side and puts an arm around* HUMPTY, *who accepts his assistance.*)

BURLY. That's right, prove it.

PAPA. Everything is in order. Perfectly legal. I have a will. (*Reaches into his pocket and begins to hunt.*)

GUNDER. Papa, why didn't you tell us!

PAMELA. We didn't know you had a will.

PAPA. I have a will. It says that I may live here as long as I like. (*Hunting.*) My Uncle Tony was a fine man.

WINNIE (*longing to help*). What does a will look like, Papa?

PAPA. Just a little piece of paper . . . folded neatly. (*The* BOYS *are helping* PAPA *turn pockets of his clown suit inside out.*) No, that's not it. (*Pulls out many things.*)

BURLY. You haven't got a will.

PAPA. Hold your horses. Hold your horses. I've just misplaced it. Very careless that way. Put it in a safe place and can't quite remember.

PAMELA. Oh, Papa, I wish you wouldn't forget so often.

PAPA. Forget? Who said I'd forgotten? I know perfectly well I put it in my pocket.

ERIC. This is your clown suit. It's in your other coat pocket.

PAPA. Of course. How stupid. I'll get it now. (*Starts for wall;* BURLY *stops him.*)

BURLY. No, you don't. This way. You're getting out of here.

PAPA. You'll regret this haste, my good man. You'll regret it. Don't push.

BURLY. Get going or I'll have the law on you!

PAPA (*pointing to his pennant on the pole*). The law says "possession is nine-tenths of the law."

BURLY (*advancing so threateningly that* PAPA *and group are backing off R*). We'll see about that. (BURLY *stands triumphantly as the scene is cleared. Suddenly he notes the costume trunk which has been left. He picks it up and carries it off L.* HUMPTY *is staring off R when* PAPA *looks over the wall and throws a handful of colored balls at him.*)

PAPA. We'll be back. We will. (HUMPTY *is so startled he sits down as if pushed.* BURLY *returns, picks him up and they both stare the way the group has gone.*)

CURTAIN

ACT TWO

SCENE: *The same as Act One, the following afternoon. The Pompino flag is still flying above the wall.*

As the curtain opens, HUMPTY sits on the ground trying to fix the cords of a yellow silk pennant with a rampant red dragon in the center. BURLY is stage L "working out." He wears ankle shoes, socks, shorts, sweat shirt.

HUMPTY (*calling*). Burly. Burly. Stop. (BURLY'*s feet beat a light tattoo as he spars with an imaginary partner. He breathes heavily.*) Burly, I can't talk to you when you're doing that. Come over here. (BURLY *grunts and starts moving toward* HUMPTY *without breaking his rhythm of punching and dodging.*) You've been doing that almost an hour.

BURLY. Gotta keep in condition.

HUMPTY. But I have work to do. (BURLY *continues his work-out.*) Burly, I want you to put this pennant up.

BURLY (*boxing fast and furious*). Okay. Okay. This'll be the winder-upper. I'll finish this guy off fast. (HUMPTY *begins to watch, gets very excited, rises to imitate, punches feebly. As* BURLY *ends,* HUMPTY *is trying to imitate footwork.*)

HUMPTY. Come on. I'll fight you. (*Raining blows.*)

BURLY (*surprised and almost ready to encourage*). Hey. No fighting for you.

HUMPTY. I could fight you. (BURLY *catches his wrists.*) I could fight. I could fight.

BURLY (*soothingly*). Sure you could. But one hooker from me and you'd be busted up good.

HUMPTY. I'm going to fight sometime.

BURLY. Sure. Sure. Here. Untie these mitts. (HUMPTY *unties them.* BURLY *goes behind bush and returns with bath towel which he wraps round his neck.*)

HUMPTY. Here. Put this pennant up.

BURLY. Sure thing. What you flying a pennant for?

HUMPTY. I have to make it legal.

BURLY. How's that?

HUMPTY. We have to show we own this wall.

BURLY. We own it all right.

HUMPTY. Papa Pompino says possession is nine-tenths of the law.

BURLY (*jumping into action, taking flag onto wall and fastening it to pole*). We'll get that old geezer's flag down in no time. (*He throws the Pompino flag down and* HUMPTY *puts it in his pocket after smoothing it out.* BURLY *holds the Dumbtop flag out for everyone to see.*) Say, what kind of an animal is this?

HUMPTY. A raging red dragon. He belonged to my ancestors.

BURLY. You know, Dumbtop, that guy ought to be one of my ancestors. (*Jumps down.*) Yes, sir. When I get mad, I'm burning up. Fire's coming out of my mouth. Just like this guy. I'm a raging red dragon.

HUMPTY. You said it wasn't good to fight when you got mad.

BURLY (*reluctantly*). Sure. That's right. Some little guy with a cool head's apt to lay one in. Unexpected. See? Like this. (*He begins to play two roles at once—himself and his cool opponent. He talks steadily.*) I'm mad. I'm breathing fire. I get to hitting wide. (*Dances around making wide hits. Suddenly changes roles.*) All of a sudden, this cool little guy comes in with a left to the jaw. (*He punches, changes roles and staggers back as if hurt.*) I'm caught off guard. I'm staggering, I'm on the ropes, I slip, I'm down. (*He falls. Then he drops the imaginary game and gets up swaggering.*) But don't you worry, Dumbtop. Nobody's going to catch Binkowitz off guard. (*Notices that* HUMPTY *has stopped listening and is staring off R.*) Aw, quit worrying about those kids. They know better than to get me sore.

HUMPTY. I wonder if they found the will. (BURLY *makes a gesture of contempt.*) Burly, I don't think Papa Pompino could own this wall.

BURLY. Of course he couldn't.

HUMPTY. But if he did have a will . . .

BURLY (*airily*). He was talking through his hat. Strictly through his hat.

HUMPTY. Anyway, I've been investigating.

BURLY. You what?

HUMPTY. If Pompino claims this is his wall, his claims should be investigated.

BURLY. They should?

HUMPTY. Here's what I've found out. (*Takes card from pocket.*) E. H. Ridgewood owned this hill before my father bought it. Before that, Eli Hunt and Samuel Sneed owned it. Before that, Ezra Adams owned some of it. Hiram Oaks owned a little more and George Abercrombie owned most of all.

BURLY (*dumbfounded*). How do you know all that?

HUMPTY. I telephoned my father's attorney.

BURLY. Your father's attor . . . Well, of all . . . Well, I'll be . . . Smart. That's what.

HUMPTY. He gave me a great deal of information. But he couldn't find anything about Pompino owning the land.

BURLY (*relieved*). Like I told you.

HUMPTY. Maybe his uncle wasn't named Pompino.

BURLY. Forget it.

HUMPTY. I'm going to find out what his uncle's name was. (*Dreams.*) Burly, if Papa Pompino did have a will and I found it, the Bambinos would think I was their friend, wouldn't they?

BURLY (*looking at him closely*). Sure, sure.

HUMPTY. And if he did own this wall, the Bambinos could give their show. They have one hundred and sixty tickets. I could buy them all.

BURLY (*figuring this dream has gone far enough*). There isn't going to be any show around here. That old clown doesn't own this wall. You proved it yourself.

HUMPTY (*brisk and practical again*). I said I was going to prove he couldn't possibly own it.

BURLY. Well, I'm heading for the showers. Come on.

HUMPTY (*lapsing into a dream again*). I must get them to talk to me. (*Pulls several colored balls from his pockets.*)

BURLY. Jumpin' catfish! Where'd you get those?

HUMPTY. I picked them up. If the Bambinos come back, I'll throw them. I know how I can get them to talk. Burly, bring the trunk with their costumes.

BURLY. Nothing doing.

HUMPTY. They need them for the show.

BURLY. Teach 'em a lesson not to leave their junk lying around.

HUMPTY. You didn't give them a chance to pick anything up. We're going to leave the trunk out here. They'll come back to get it and I'll ask them a lot of questions.

BURLY. Just let me lay eyes on any one of them . . . or that old clown. . . . I'll throw them all in jail. (HUMPTY *has marched off for the trunk.* BURLY *follows.* ERIC *and* JOHN *appear from opposite side, note the Dumbtop flag.*)

ERIC. Look at that. He took Papa's flag down and put up his own. (*Jumps to wall.*)

JOHN. Don't. Papa wouldn't want us to tear anything down. We gotta find his will and prove he owns this wall. (PAMELA *and* MARINA *enter.*)

PAMELA. Isn't Papa here yet?

ERIC. How can we tell? That prizefighter's been guarding the place for hours.

MARINA. Can we start hunting for the will?

JOHN. It isn't the will really, it's just a piece of paper with a clue on it.

PAMELA. Why does Papa always forget where he puts things?

ERIC. If he could only remember what the clue said. (FELIX *and* GUNDER *enter.*)

FELIX. Isn't he here? (*Four shake their heads.*)

GUNDER. Then where is he? We've been over every inch of this estate.

MARINA (*alarmed*). Maybe something's happened to him.

JOHN (*equally worried*). Oh, nothing's happened to him.

PAMELA. What if that awful man got him?

JOHN. That old hulk? He couldn't catch Papa.

MARINA. Not unless Papa fell asleep.

FELIX. Papa's too smart to fall asleep around here now. (*A scream is heard off* L. WINNIE *and* TSING LING *run on, very frightened.*)

WINNIE. He's out there.

BOYS (*all talking at once*). Who's there?

TSING LING. He's hiding. He jumped at us.

BOYS. Who jumped?

WINNIE. Humpty Dumpty Dumbtop.

ERIC. I'll get him.

GUNDER. Wait.

ERIC. We can't have that brat hanging around when we're hunting for the will.

GUNDER. It's no good chasing him off once. We gotta get rid of him for a long, long time. Let's think of a way. (*They all rack their brains.*)

BURLY (*calling from far off*). Dumbtop.

JOHN. Scare him. We gotta scare him so bad he'll run home and won't come out for days and days.

GUNDER. I don't like to do it, but we gotta.

BURLY (*calling closer*). Dumbtop.

MARINA (*terrified*). It's Burly.

GUNDER. Don't get excited. Everybody hide but don't go far away. We gotta catch Dumbtop alone. (ALL *vanish.* ERIC *goes over wall as* HUMPTY *enters.*)

HUMPTY. I saw you. (*Goes to wall but no one answers.* BURLY *comes up behind him.*)

BURLY. Hey, what's the idea running off where I can't find you?

HUMPTY (*haughtily*). You didn't bring the trunk.

BURLY (*with sarcasm*). How can I lug a trunk around when I'm looking for my precious little treasure?

HUMPTY. Bring it now.

BURLY. Okay. But you come, too.

HUMPTY. I'll wait here.

BURLY. And when I get back, you're gone again? Oh, no. (*He suddenly lifts* HUMPTY *to the wall.*) If you want to wait, you can sit right there.

HUMPTY (*really frightened*). Take me down. Take me down.

BURLY. Just sit still, my little basket of eggs, and you'll be safe. (*Goes off L.* BOYS *see their chance to scare* HUMPTY, *who is clutching the wall, almost afraid to breathe.* FELIX *and* GUNDER *saunter on with elaborate casualness.* NOTE TO DIRECTOR: *The following scene is to be played for comedy.* HUMPTY's *fear is a psychological problem but his craving to get in touch with the group is as strong as his fear. The conflict within himself causes the "shakes." The* BOYS *produce terror through making fun rather than gangster tactics.*)

FELIX (*as if pleased*). Well, if it isn't little Dumbtop. All alone, too. Aren't you scared to be way out here all by yourself?

JOHN. You ought to keep that bodyguard of yours around.

GUNDER. John, you run along and keep Burly company. Let us know if he starts back this way.

JOHN. Shall I give the usual? (*He demonstrates a war whoop.* GUNDER *nods.* JOHN *goes after* BURLY. FELIX, GUNDER, *and* ERIC *appear to be concerned about* HUMPTY.)

ERIC. Little Dumbtop shouldn't be out here alone, should he, Gunder?

GUNDER. Oh, we'll take good care of him.

FELIX. Look how his teeth are chattering.

HUMPTY. I want . . . I want . . . I . . . I . . .

ERIC. Don't be so scared, Dumbtop. We aren't mad about yesterday. Are we, Felix?

FELIX (*bitterly*). Oh, not at all. We've forgotten all about the way our show was spoiled.

ERIC. And the way our costume trunk was stolen.

HUMPTY. I . . . I . . . (*He wants to say that the trunk is coming, but can't.*)

ERIC. Wow! Look at him shake.

FELIX. Hold on tight. That wall's going to fly away with you.

ERIC (*as if protecting* HUMPTY). Don't make it fly, Eric. He's never tried riding a wall before.

FELIX. I'm sorry this is such a high one. Bucks like an old bronco. He'll probably have all his bones busted when he comes down.

ERIC. Just sit still, my little basket of eggs, and you'll be safe.

FELIX. If you ask me, he's going to shake himself off right now. (FELIX *and* ERIC *grab* HUMPTY's *legs as if to steady him.*)

ERIC (*to* GUNDER). Okay, we've captured him. What'll we do with him?

GUNDER (*very ominously*). Dumbtop, it's my business to warn you. You're not safe around this place. (*War whoop off.*) We'll give you one chance, Dumbtop. Take that body-guard away and don't ever show your face around here again. Next time I won't be able to keep my men from tearing you into ribbons. (BOYS *back off slowly ad libbing muttered threats. Another war whoop is heard and* JOHN *runs on. He jumps the wall right beside* HUMPTY *and disappears.* BURLY *dashes on.*)

BURLY. What are you yelling for? (HUMPTY is shaking so
hard he couldn't have yelled. BURLY lifts him down and
HUMPTY collapses. His legs won't hold him up.) Hey, are
you sick?

HUMPTY. You shouldn't . . . have . . . put . . . me up
. . . so high. My mother told you.

BURLY (filled with remorse, for he sees that HUMPTY is seriously upset). You poor kid. I must have been out of my
mind. I better take you home quick. (WINNIE looks on
and HUMPTY sees her.)

HUMPTY (loudly). They didn't really scare me.

BURLY (suspiciously). Who? Who didn't scare you? Say,
have those kids been back here?

HUMPTY (trying to distract him). Nobody's here, Burly. Get
the trunk.

BURLY. Golly. I dropped it when I heard you war whooping.
(Runs off for it.)

HUMPTY (calling). Winnie, come out. I want to talk to you.
(BURLY hurries back and drops the trunk. HUMPTY seems
to have recovered slightly from the shakes and helps open
it.) Hurry. Give me the king's robe. When I'm king she'll
talk to me.

BURLY. Who'll talk to you?

HUMPTY. Queen of Hearts.

BURLY (scratching head in familiar gesture). You're sure a
queer one. (HUMPTY has donned the robe and crown.)

HUMPTY. Lift me up to the wall. (BURLY exclaims in surprise.) Lift me. Quickly.

BURLY. You was just up there—shaking like a bunch of rattles.

HUMPTY. I'm the king now.

BURLY (feeling his head for temperature). You're feverish.

HUMPTY. Burly. Put me up. Right now.

BURLY. Honest, if you break those bones nothing can put you together again.

HUMPTY. You can guard me.

BURLY (*pacing*). I shouldn't have done it.

HUMPTY (*yelling with rage*). Put me up.

BURLY. What'll I tell your old man?

HUMPTY. You don't have to tell him.

BURLY. But he asks me. He asks me every night.

HUMPTY (*taking a deep breath and swelling up*). Tell him I am the king . . . Ruler of the Indies. Tsar of all the Russias. High Potentate of all the Persias. Imperial Majesty of the Babylonians. Supreme Ruler of the Orient. And I made you put me up.

BURLY. Yes, your Majesty. (*Lifts* HUMPTY *to wall. Picks up helmet and spear from trunk and begins to march as a guard.*) Anything you say. (HUMPTY *is looking for* WINNIE, *but she does not appear.*) Anything your heart desires. How long do you figure on sitting upon the throne, your Majesty?

HUMPTY. Keep marching.

BURLY. Yes, your Majesty. (PAPA *looks out and steps back quickly.*)

HUMPTY (*frantic*). March clear around the wall, Burly. (BURLY *whirls and goes off.* HUMPTY *calls.*) Papa. Papa Pompino. Come up. I want to talk to you. (PAPA *looks out and nods a vigorous refusal.*) I'll get you anything you want to eat. (PAPA *stares as if he doesn't understand this trick, then backs off as* BURLY *marches on.*)

BURLY. All's well, your Majesty.

HUMPTY. Burly, I'm getting hungry.

BURLY. Now that you mention it, so am I. (PAPA *looks out and rubs stomach.*)

HUMPTY. You could go and ask Agnes to fix us a feast.

BURLY. Fine idea. What shall I order?

HUMPTY. I'll think. You write my order down.

BURLY. I have no paper.

HUMPTY. Write it on the ground. That way you'll remember. (BURLY *picks up stick, stands half turned to wall, ready to write on ground.*) I want . . . I want . . .

PAPA (*popping up behind wall and speaking in a stage whisper*). Pumpernickel.

HUMPTY (*repeats the order to* BURLY). Pumpernickel.

BURLY (*repeats*). Pumpernickel. (*Each uses a different tone of voice so that the orders are sung out in three notes.*)

PAPA. Bologna. (HUMPTY *and* BURLY *repeat. The speed of the orders increases to a high climax with* BURLY *rushing off.*) Cold fried chicken. (HUMPTY *and* BURLY *repeat.*) Pumpkin pie. (HUMPTY *and* BURLY *repeat.*) Apples and grapes. (HUMPTY *and* BURLY *repeat.*) Chocolate cake. (HUMPTY *and* BURLY *repeat.*)

BURLY. Golly, I won't be able to carry all this. Be right back. (*Runs off L.* PAPA *half climbs on the wall.*)

PAPA. You mean we're really going to have all this delicious food?

HUMPTY. Of course.

PAPA. It isn't just pretend? (HUMPTY *nods* "no.") It's too good to be true. (PAPA *climbs up beside* HUMPTY.) Very considerate of you, your Majesty. I was feeling decidedly faint from hunger.

HUMPTY. Did you find the will?

PAPA (*starts to go*). Hm . . . not exactly.

HUMPTY. I might help you. I'm good at finding things.

PAPA (*still eyes him suspiciously but decides to stay around*). Thank you, but I don't see how you could help find this

little item when I can't recall myself where I put it. (*He
takes out his watch and swings it from its long chain.*) Just
plain can't recall where I put it.

HUMPTY. Papa. How long have you lived here?

PAPA (*calculating by the stars*). Seventy-two moons, three
hundred and twelve Sundays.

HUMPTY (*after a very slight pause*). That's about six years.

PAPA. Say, nothing wrong with your head.

HUMPTY (*smiling a little apologetically*). Oh, no. It's just my
bones. It's dangerous for me to run or jump or climb or
anything.

PAPA. Did you fly up here?

HUMPTY. Burly put me up. I'm sitting very still.

PAPA. Very sensible.

HUMPTY. Papa, did your uncle live on this wall, too?

PAPA. He did, and my great uncle before him.

HUMPTY (*tensely*). What was your uncle's name?

PAPA. Tony.

HUMPTY. I mean his last name.

PAPA. Pompino. Same as mine.

HUMPTY. Are you sure it wasn't Adams?

PAPA. Quite sure.

HUMPTY. Then what was your great uncle's name?

PAPA. Giuseppe.

HUMPTY. Giuseppe Adams or Ridgewood?

PAPA. Certainly not. It was Giuseppe Pompino.

HUMPTY. Are you sure he didn't have any other name . . .
like Oaks or Abercrombie?

PAPA. Don't you think I know my own uncle's name?

HUMPTY (*puzzled*). If his name was Pompino, he couldn't
have given you this wall.

PAPA (*indignantly*). You're trying to trick me. (BURLY ap-

pears suddenly, carrying a hamper. He has discarded the
helmet and spear and put on trousers. AGNES follows, also
carrying a basket. BURLY sees PAPA and the chase is on.)
BURLY. No use running away.
PAPA (appears on wall and shakes fist). I'm not running away.
I live here.
HUMPTY. Don't chase him, Burly. (BURLY pays no attention.
PAPA runs across front and AGNES tries to stop him. PAPA
eludes both AGNES and BURLY. HUMPTY yells instructions
to all three. PAPA trips and falls once. When he rises, his
watch is on the ground. HUMPTY sees it at once.) The
watch. Burly, give me the watch. Don't step on it. (BURLY
obeys without knowing what he's doing. Hands watch to
HUMPTY, then turns to yell at PAPA, who seems to have
run off.)
BURLY. I told you not to come back here. If you come back
again, I'll grind you to a pulp. I'll flatten you out like a
pancake. (AGNES is patting BURLY on the arm to soothe
him.) I'm fighting mad. I'm seeing red.
AGNES. Keep your temper. Calm down. Your temper always
causes trouble. (HUMPTY has been examining the watch.
Opening the back cover, he discovers a folded piece of
paper. It flutters to the ground.)
HUMPTY. Get the paper. Give it to me. (AGNES hands it to
him.) This may be the will. (He reads while AGNES begins
to unpack the basket. She hands BURLY a chicken leg
which he promptly and furiously gnaws.) Listen to this,
Burly. "Start where quartz lies rose on brown. Ten to the
right. One up. Nine down. If you stop to nibble Eden's
fruit, beware the tread of a stealthy boot." What does it
mean? I know. It's a clue. It's a clue that tells where
Papa's will is.

BURLY (*finally listening*). Say it again. We'll find it.

HUMPTY. "Start where quartz lies rose on brown." (*He leans to look at stones in the wall.*) There's a lot of quartz in this wall, Burly. (*Reads again.*) "Ten to the right. One up. Nine down." It could mean some way of counting stones. There may be a secret niche in the wall. (*Reads again.*) "If you stop to nibble Eden's fruit . . ."

BURLY. That's apples.

HUMPTY. Get me down, Burly. We need tools for digging. (BURLY *lifts him down promptly.*) Agnes, wait for us. (HUMPTY *takes off crown and robe.* BURLY *puts them in trunk, carrying it as they go off L.* AGNES *shrugs, finds a comfortable place to sit, takes a piece of chicken from the basket and nibbles daintily.* PAPA *looks on, rubs his hands, tiptoes up behind* AGNES *and whistles shrilly. She jumps.*)

PAPA (*looking in basket and helping himself*). Anything left?

AGNES. Get out of here.

PAPA. Tut . . . tut . . . (*Dancing lightly out of her reach.*) Ladies should never shout. (AGNES *chases* PAPA *with a chicken bone held like a big stick. He dodges, reaches in basket for another bite of something, gets a chicken leg, challenges her to duel.* BOYS' *voices are heard off R.*)

AGNES (*frightened*). What's that?

PAPA. My gang.

AGNES. Burly.

PAPA. No use calling him. You're caught. (*She runs off L screaming.* PAPA *clicks his heels as he leaps in the air and sits down beside the basket.* BAMBINOS *enter.*)

ALL (*ad lib.*). Papa. Where have you been? We've looked everywhere for you.

PAMELA (*exasperated*). And what are you doing now?

PAPA. Feasting, my child. Beautiful feasting. Have some?

GUNDER. Where did you go, Papa?

PAPA. My Bambinos, gather round. I have been on a long trip to the village to consult my old lawyer. I thought he might advise me about my property.

ALL (ad lib.). What did he say? Tell us.

PAPA (ruefully). Unfortunately, he said he couldn't do a thing unless I found the will.

PAMELA. Which means you have to find the paper with the clue on it first.

WINNIE. Think hard, Papa. You can remember where you put it. It wasn't in your pocket.

PAPA. Of course, I remember where I put it. I put it right here in my hat band. (Takes off his hat, searches wildly.) Hm . . . that means I took it out of here and put it someplace else.

ALL (ad lib.). Think. Try to remember. We've got to find it.

PAPA (leaping to feet). My watch. I put it in the back of my watch. (He digs in pockets.)

WINNIE. Have you lost it?

PAPA. Bless me, I don't know. I had it when I was sitting on the wall. Oh, drat that prizefighter. He made me lose my grandfather's watch.

GUNDER (sternly). What were you doing with Burly?

PAPA. Outrunning him. That's all. That boy tricked me. Tried to get me to talk. (Hunting up and down in front of wall.) It has to be here someplace. (Mutters as he tries to recall the path of the chase with BURLY.) Jumped down . . . ran that way . . . came out here . . . must have fallen out of my pocket. . . . Don't see how it could with that chain on . . . (BAMBINOS are searching too.) Might have fallen out when I ran down hill. (Starts off like a dog on the scent.)

PAMELA. Didn't you ever read the clue, Papa? Don't you re-member what it said?

PAPA (*answering absentmindedly*). "Start where quartz lies rose on brown." (*Snaps fingers to encourage himself.*) "Start where quartz lies rose on brown. . . ."

TSING LING. What does quartz mean?

FELIX. It's a stone. There's lots in these hills.

ERIC. There's lots of quartz right in this wall.

PAMELA. Go on, Papa.

PAPA. "Six to the right . . . ten down." No, that's not right. "Seven up . . . three down." No. No. You see, my Uncle Tony thought it was a good joke to make me hunt for things. He was always writing clues like that. He said this one was about a will but it didn't make much sense and I was tired of playing his games, so I never paid enough attention.

PAMELA. Try to remember it, Papa. Start fast and don't stop.

PAPA (*fast*). "Start where quartz lies rose on brown. Ten to the right. One up. Nine down. If you stop to nibble Eden's fruit, beware the tread of a stealthy boot." That's it.

FELIX. Then it's in this wall.

PAPA. Oh, it couldn't be. That's too close to home.

FELIX. There's quartz in the wall. One up and nine down could mean counting stones.

MARINA. Eden's fruit means apples and there's the apple tree.

GUNDER. Beware the tread of a stealthy boot. What's that?

ERIC. That means look out for Burly.

FELIX. Where do we begin to count? (BAMBINOS *try to figure it out.*)

JOHN. If Burly catches us, he'll put us in jail.

GUNDER. We won't let him catch us.

ERIC. He goes in to dinner at six o'clock. We can hunt then.

GUNDER. Meet back here at six sharp. (ALL go off except PAPA, who is still looking for watch.)

ERIC. Come on, Papa.

PAPA. Coming. (Continues to hunt. Afternoon sunlight is fading. PAPA leans on wall, weary of the excitement. Climbs up to his seat in the apple tree and seems sad. He leans back and suddenly drops off to sleep. HUMPTY and BURLY return with tools. Go immediately to end of wall. HUMPTY begins counting stones as if he had mentally solved the problem in advance. BURLY is absorbed. Gets down on hands and knees.)

HUMPTY. We can try here. Get this stone out. (BURLY works at it with a small tool.) It's coming. Go on. There. You've got it. Lift it out. Now. (Puts stone on ground, hand in hole.) There's a hole here. Something in it, too.

BURLY. Let me feel. (Puts his arm in.) Feels like a box in there. It is. (Pulling it out.) What do you know?

HUMPTY. Can you open it? (BURLY pries it open. HUMPTY examines contents. BURLY stands up stiffly. Turns and sees PAPA. He makes a gesture of victory with one clenched fist, then turns and pulls HUMPTY to his feet. HUMPTY grabs the box. BURLY swings him up to the wall.) What are you doing?

BURLY (pleading). Just sit there one minute. Just one minute. (HUMPTY is so absorbed with a paper he's found that he ignores BURLY. BURLY moves like a panther beside PAPA. He lets out a war whoop and PAPA sits up. It's too late. BURLY grabs him as he leaps to ground. They struggle but BURLY is stronger. HUMPTY yells desperately at BURLY but his shouts are unheeded.)

BURLY. I told you I'd throw you in jail and now I'm going

to do it. (*He is dragging the struggling* PAPA *off* R. PAPA
is ad libbing wildly and fighting like a bantam.)

HUMPTY (*stops his yelling and a tense silence settles; he suddenly realizes he's alone and on the wall; his voice is low
and tense*). Get me down. Burly. Get me down. Somebody
get me down. (*He clutches the box in his arms and con-
siders jumping. He's obviously almost paralyzed with
fright. After several agonizing attempts, he slides off, half
lands on his feet, crumbles, and falls. For a second he
seems stunned, then he moves slightly. He begins to crawl
toward the bush, gets part way and folds up completely.*

CURTAIN

ACT THREE

SCENE: *The same. Sunset.*

HUMPTY *is hidden by the bush.* AGNES *is heard calling
off* L.

AGNES. Burly. Oh, Burly. (*Enters.*) Oh, dear. (*Pauses, hears
whistling off R, runs to* BURLY *as he enters with a swinging
stride.*) Burly, you're so late.

BURLY. Well, I finally fixed that Pompino so he'll stay away
from here.

AGNES. What did you do to him?

BURLY. Put him in jail for trespassing.

AGNES. Where's little Dumbtop?

BURLY. Right— (*Stares at wall.*) He was right here.

AGNES (*horrified*). You surely didn't leave him here.

BURLY. He couldn't get off that wall by himself.

AGNES. Oh, Burly. What will Mr. Dumbtop say?

BURLY. He's been kidnapped. Agnes, he's been kidnapped.

AGNES. Oh, let's get away from here.

BURLY. Do you think I'd go and leave that poor little kid? (AGNES *sobs.*) Keep quiet. I gotta figure out which way they went. (*Going to wall.*) First, they dragged him off the wall. Any marks on the ground? Any blood? (*Drops to knees to look ground over.*) Here. Here's exactly where he landed. He must have been scared stiff. Listen. (*Whistle off R.*) He's that way. (*Grabs* AGNES *by the arm and runs off. The* BAMBINOS *come on cautiously, one at a time.* JOHN *acts as scout. Motions to others.*)

JOHN. We gotta work fast. (GUNDER *gives directions as each enters.*)

GUNDER. Eric, you watch the path to the house. Winnie, you stand guard on the wall. (JOHN *and* GUNDER *boost her up as* ERIC *goes off L.* FELIX *and* PAMELA *enter together.*)

PAMELA. Where shall we start counting?

FELIX. Start where quartz lies rose on brown. . . . Hey! Look at this big stone.

PAMELA. There's a hole in the wall, too. (TSING LING *and* MARINA *have entered and all stare, bending down to watch* FELIX, *who is on his hands and knees, reaching into hole.*)

FELIX. It's a hiding place all right, a big one.

GUNDER. Anything in it?

FELIX. No. (*Lets himself fall into a sitting position.*)

PAMELA. Somebody's been here or that stone wouldn't have been on the ground.

GUNDER. Dumbtop found the watch and the clue. He's been here.

TSING LING. Maybe he didn't find anything. Maybe it wasn't the right place. (ALL *pause as a great groan comes from the bush.*)

MARINA (*fearfully*). What was it? (GIRLS *huddle together.* BOYS *can't quite make up their minds what to do.* GUNDER *finally walks over cautiously.*)

FELIX. Sounds like a wounded animal.

GUNDER. It's Dumbtop! He's hurt. (ALL *rush over.* GUNDER *and* JOHN *lift* HUMPTY's *apparently lifeless form to C.*)

MARINA. You aren't supposed to move anybody till you know where they're hurt.

WINNIE (*on knees beside* HUMPTY). Get some water. (*Hands handkerchief to* FELIX.) Quick. (FELIX *picks up bucket and goes off.*) He's trying to say something. (*Puts her ear down close to his lips.*) He's saying, "Papa . . . Papa." Go on, Humpty. We're listening. Oh! He says, "Help Papa."

FELIX. Where is he?

WINNIE (*listening closely*). Louder, Humpty. (*Gasps.*) Burly got him.

ALL (*ad lib.*). No! Where is he? We've got to rescue him. (FELIX *returns with bucket and wet cloth.*)

WINNIE. Humpty, do you know where Papa is? (*Listens.*) Oh, he's so hurt he can't talk.

GUNDER. We'll divide up and look all over this place . . . but let's think first.

FELIX. Barn.

PAMELA. Summerhouse on the hill.

TSING LING. Hayloft.

WINNIE. Wait. Wait. He's trying. Go on, Humpty. He says . . . He says . . . (*horrified*) "in jail." (ALL *ad lib. excitement.*) Be quiet. He says, "Get him out."

GUNDER. Let's go. (*War whoops and* ERIC *returns on the run.*)

WINNIE (*jumping to her feet*). What about Humpty? We can't leave him alone.

GUNDER. You and Tsing Ling stay with him. (*Others exit R.*

TSING LING *takes off her jacket and rolls it up as a pillow for* HUMPTY'S *head.* WINNIE *adjusts the damp cloth.*)

TSING LING. It's awful to be hurt.

HUMPTY (*groaning*). Fell off.

WINNIE. What did you say, Humpty?

HUMPTY. Fell off.

TSING LING. Where did you fall?

HUMPTY. The wall.

WINNIE. Did somebody push you?

TSING LING. Somebody pushed me once and I fell off.

HUMPTY (*groaning*). All broken. Bones . . .

WINNIE. What's broken? Oh, dear. It might be his ankle or his arm.

HUMPTY. All my bones broken.

WINNIE. They couldn't all be broken.

HUMPTY. All broken.

TSING LING. Once I fell down two flights of stairs and I didn't break anything.

WINNIE. Once I fell out of a window and broke my collar bone. Humpty, does your collar bone hurt?

HUMPTY. Everything broken. Never get well.

TSING LING. Oh, don't say that.

HUMPTY. Bones just like eggs.

WINNIE. Well, that's foolish.

HUMPTY. All my bones are special.

WINNIE. That's funny. You look just like everybody else.

HUMPTY. Break just like that. (*Claps hands.*)

WINNIE (*relieved*). At least your hands aren't broken or you couldn't clap.

TSING LING. His arms couldn't be broken either.

WINNIE. Humpty, maybe you aren't broken at all.

TSING LING. Maybe you just hurt all over.

HUMPTY (*refusing to stir*). All the king's horses and all the king's men . . .

TSING LING. That's just an old nursery rhyme.

WINNIE. Humpty, you have to put yourself together again.

HUMPTY (*lifts his head in surprise*). How can I?

WINNIE. Like this. Move your hand. (*Moves left wrist in a circle for him.*)

TSING LING. It moves fine. Now do this one. (*Moves* HUMPTY's *right wrist.*)

WINNIE. Now lift your arm. (*Lifts it for him.*) Hold it way out.

TSING LING. This one, too. (*Moves other arm.*) See, Humpty? No arms broken.

WINNIE. Roll your head around. (HUMPTY *does.*) Now your foot. (*Helps.*)

TSING LING. Now this one. (*They work with great care and concern but with a growing excitement.*)

WINNIE. Now your knee. Lift it up. That's right. (*Helps.*)

TSING LING. This one, too. (*Stepping back to look at him critically.*) Humpty, I do believe you're going to be all right.

WINNIE. You were mostly scared.

TSING LING. And you feel sore where you bumped.

WINNIE. Now you must sit up. (*They pull him to sitting position.*) Humpty, you can do anything. You're all right.

HUMPTY. Can I catch a ball?

WINNIE. Of course. But you have to stand up first. Here. Hold my hand.

TSING LING. Hold mine, too. (*They pull gently. He gets halfway up and sits down.*) Too bad. Try again. (*They pull again. Halfway up, his knees cave in and he flops.*)

HUMPTY. Can't.

WINNIE. You can. You almost made it. Here we go. (*They pull. He gets up and flops.*)

HUMPTY. Can't.

WINNIE (*stamps foot*). Don't say that word again. You can.

HUMPTY (*tries and fails again*). No use. Call Burly.

WINNIE (*standing away, hands on hips*). Burly can't do a thing for you, Humpty Dumpty Dumbtop. You're just a spoiled brat. You've let your mother and your father and that Agnes and Burly and everybody scare you. You can do anything you want to do.

TSING LING. You'd like to catch a ball like all of us, wouldn't you, Humpty? Keep thinking about catching balls and climbing the wall and running. (*Holds out hand.*) Come on. Think hard. (*They pull and get him to his feet. His knees shake but he stays up. GIRLS ad lib. their praise.*)

HUMPTY. My knees.

TSING LING. Oh, don't mind them. Knees are always shaky after a fall.

WINNIE. You had a bad fright but it's all over now.

TSING LING. Let him stand alone. (*Moves back, HUMPTY staggers.*) Don't give up.

WINNIE. Here. Catch. (*Throws a ball but it sails past because HUMPTY doesn't even reach for it. He's just realized that he's had a bad fall and that absolutely nothing is wrong with him. Elation grows in him.*)

HUMPTY. Look at me. I'm not a basket of eggs. No bones broken. Throw the ball. (WINNIE *throws another but* HUMPTY *misses.*)

TSING LING (*picking it up*). He wasn't ready for it. Throw another. (*Misses again.*) Hold your hands like this. (*Catches one.*) Good. You get to keep that one.

HUMPTY (*really in awe of himself*). I can do anything. I want to climb on the wall. I want to climb up the ladder.

WINNIE. Where is it?

HUMPTY. Beside the path.

WINNIE. I'll get it. (TSING LING *joins her and they bring the ladder back.*)

HUMPTY. You don't need to help. (*Goes up the ladder slowly but doesn't stop; is awkward at getting off onto the wall but makes it.*) Nobody can ever keep me from climbing again. Not Burly or my father or Agnes or even my mother. Get me the box.

WINNIE. What box?

HUMPTY. It must be under that bush. I had it when I fell. (WINNIE *gets it and hands it up.*) It belongs to Papa Pompino. (*Voices off R.* PAPA, *in a rage, enters with* BAMBINOS.)

PAPA. Just let me get my hands on him. Where is he? (*Sees* HUMPTY.) Where's that big baboon of yours? Throwing me in jail. Me! a Pompino! Well, he couldn't keep me locked up. Every policeman in this town is a friend of mine.

HUMPTY. I'm sorry, Papa. Burly was seeing red.

PAPA. Well, I'm seeing red now. Where is he? (*Begins to shadow box.* HUMPTY *holds out box containing the will.*)

HUMPTY. I found something for you, Papa.

PAPA. Keep it.

HUMPTY. But it's yours.

WINNIE. Look at it, Papa.

PAPA. I don't want to look at anything except that moldy old prizefighter.

JOHN (*watching with alarm as* PAPA *continues to shadow box*). You wouldn't try to fight Burly!

PAPA. I would. (BOYS *and* GIRLS *protest. Ad lib.*). I may not be a heavyweight but I'm going to pick off the title for the bantams.

ERIC. You're going to need help.

PAPA. I'm seeing red. Bright, flaming red.

JOHN. Think what you're doing, Papa. Burly's a real fighter.

PAPA. Well, if he thinks he's the only piece of brawn and muscle ever stepped into a ring, I'll show him. (AGNES *runs on. Screams.* BURLY *enters.*) Come out, you hulking alligator. (BURLY *stops in surprise at seeing him.*)

BURLY. How'd you get out?

PAPA. There's no cage in the world strong enough to hold a Pompino. Limber up.

BURLY. Me fight you?

PAPA. Yes! Me. Vespuccio Pompino.

BURLY. Why, you . . . you . . . (*Almost chokes with fury.* BOYS *try to hold* PAPA.)

PAPA (*to* BOYS). You stay out of this. All of you. Stand back. It's my fight. (*To* BURLY.) Take a good look at the scenery. This is the last time you'll be gazing out of those pretty blue eyes. (BURLY *lunges.* PAPA *ducks.* AGNES *screams.*)

HUMPTY. Keep cool, Papa. Keep cool. You can get him. (BAMBINOS *and* AGNES *form a vocal background for the fight.* HUMPTY *stays on the wall shouting instructions.* BURLY *gets madder and madder, starts hitting wide but catches* PAPA *off guard at last.* PAPA *falls.*)

BAMBINOS. Get up, Papa. Get up. You're all right. (BURLY *is prancing, bending over ready to slug as soon as* PAPA *gets up.* HUMPTY *makes a leap from the wall and comes in with an unexpected right to* BURLY's *jaw.* BURLY *staggers, loses balance, falls, hits head.*)

BOYS (*ad lib.*). Zowie! Did you see that? A haymaker. The kid himself did it. (*They pat* HUMPTY *on the back.* GUNDER *and*

JOHN *help* PAPA *up.* HUMPTY *is appalled at what he has done and drops on his knees beside* BURLY.)

HUMPTY. Burly. Are you hurt? I didn't mean to do it. (AGNES, *on knees, too.*)

JOHN (*amazed and delighted*). He's out. (*Begins to count.* ALL *join.*) One . . . Two . . . Three . . . Four . . . Five . . . (AGNES *is pleading with* BURLY *to get up.*) Six . . . Seven . . .

AGNES. Get up, Burly. Don't let him beat you. Get up.

JOHN (*and* ALL). Eight . . . Nine . . . Ten. Out for the count. Hurray for Pompino, the winner. (*They hold* PAPA'S *arm up in traditional style.* BURLY *sits up with* HUMPTY *and* AGNES *supporting him.*)

BURLY. Wanna drink . . . from the big dipper.

ERIC. He's seeing stars.

FELIX (*to* HUMPTY). I didn't know you could fight like that.

BURLY (*his vision clearing, notes* HUMPTY). Dumbtop. You all right? Never leave you alone again.

PAPA. Seems to me he can take care of himself quite nicely.

BURLY. Oh, my poor head. (*Remains sitting and holds his head, looks at* PAPA.) Why didn't you tell me you were a fighter?

GUNDER. He didn't knock you out. Dumbtop did.

BURLY (*looking at* HUMPTY). You?

HUMPTY. Oh, Burly, I'm sorry. (BURLY *pretends to faint, then sits up.*)

BURLY. I must be some teacher. (HUMPTY *takes watch from pocket.*)

HUMPTY. Here's your watch, Papa. (*Turns to wall for box.*)

PAPA. So you did find it. (*Snaps back open.*) Clue, too. (*Takes box* HUMPTY *is holding toward him.*) What's this?

HUMPTY. Your will. I tried to give it to you but you said "Keep it."

PAPA (*taking paper from box*). My will?

ALL (*ad lib.*). Read it. Let's hear what's in it. Do you own the wall?

PAPA (*reading*). "Be it known to one and all that the men of the Pompino family have served my family faithfully and well since the days of the Revolution."

BURLY (*becoming clear-headed and threatening again*). Who signed that will?

PAPA. George Abercrombie.

HUMPTY. That's right, Burly. He owned the land once. Go on, Papa.

PAPA (*reading*). "There has been a Pompino in every battle for freedom since that day. They have worked hard for the cause of peace, making this land to prosper." (*Nods proudly.*) "They are men of good will who prefer to live under the stars even when a roof is offered them." (*Nods approval.*) "For all the years of my memory they have camped by the old stone wall on the hill. Their songs have filled the silences of the night and brightened the loneliness of days. Therefore, as a reward for service, I hereby give Giuseppe Pompino and all his heirs the old wall and twenty feet of ground on either side. They shall be the rightful owners until that day when the entire hill shall be sold as one piece of property." (*Pauses, staring.*)

BURLY. That's it. H.M.T. Dumbtop bought this entire hill. He owns it all.

PAPA (*reading again*). "Until that day when the entire hill . . ."

WINNIE. Humpty, is it true? Does your father own the entire hill?

HUMPTY (*stunned*). Yes, he does, but . . .

WINNIE (*taking* PAPA's *arm*). Oh, Papa.

PAPA. Why didn't my Uncle Tony tell me it said that? Why did he say I could live here forever? (*He looks at all the faces around him.*) Well, my Bambinos, it appears that we have been trespassing after all. We'd better be getting along now. (*His words have slowed almost to a standstill.*)

HUMPTY. You can't go.

BURLY (*softly*). Take it easy, kid.

HUMPTY. I want to read that will. (*Snatches it.*)

BURLY. What are you going to do? (HUMPTY *has taken a pencil from his pocket and is holding the paper against the side of the wall in order to write. He hands the paper back to* PAPA.)

PAPA (*reading as all the* BAMBINOS *try to read with him*). "I, H.M.T. Dumbtop III, hereby give Papa Pompino the wall and twenty-one feet on either side to live on as long as H.M.T. Dumbtop owns the hill."

BURLY. You can't do that. It isn't legal. You aren't of age.

HUMPTY. It will be legal. I'll tell my faher to get his lawyer and make it legal.

PAPA (*joyously*). Can I believe it? The wall for my own? (*He leaps to wall and his voice trembles.*) A place to live forever? Nobody asking me to move away? Everything the way I love it! (*He touches the apple tree.*) My Bambinos around me! (*He jumps down and grabs* HUMPTY's *hand.*) My boy, how can I ever thank you?

HUMPTY (*taking the Pompino flag from his pocket*). Here, Burly, put the flag up and give me mine. (BURLY *gets on wall, exchanges flags. The crowd cheers.*) Now you can

have your show. The trunk of costumes is right over
there. (*Points off L.*) Come on, Burly.

WINNIE. Where are you going?

HUMPTY. Home.

WINNIE. Are you coming back?

HUMPTY (*wistfully shakes head*). The wall belongs to Papa.
I won't ever come back.

PAPA. My wall? Nonsense. It's your wall, too. Your wall. My
wall. Our wall.

GUNDER. Let's make him a Bambino. (*Crowd shouts assent.*
FELIX *reaches into the bush and gives* PAPA *the sword.*)

PAPA. Young man, will you join our band?

HUMPTY (*almost speechless*). Me? (BAMBINOS *ad lib.* "Yes.")

PAPA. Then kneel. (HUMPTY *looks at* BURLY *as if in a trance,
then kneels.*) H.M.T. Dumbtop the third, do you promise
to be a true and helpful friend in all kinds of weather?

HUMPTY. I do.

PAPA. Will you be friendly and kind to all people, young and
old, rich and poor, white, black or yellow?

HUMPTY. I will.

PAPA (*sword on shoulder*). Then rise, Humpty Dumbtop.
You are now a Bambino. (BOYS *bang* HUMPTY *on the
shoulder.* GIRLS *grab his hand and all talk at once.*)

BURLY (*clearing throat loudly*). Uh . . . Uh . . . Mr. Pompino. Could you find any kind of a place in your outfit
for a moldy old prizefighter?

CURTAIN

PRODUCTION NOTES

SETTING   The set can be executed with drapes; cyclorama; or sky backdrop, with wings of drapes or flats. Depending on the style of the production, the apple tree may be three-dimensional with a practical seat; a two-dimensional cut-out; painted on a sky backdrop; or cut from cloth and applied to scrim. The bush and tree should be executed in keeping with the apple tree. The wall must be well constructed and solidly braced to give security to the cast and ease to the acting. Care should be taken in painting the wall that the one stone to be removed is indistinguishable from the rest as seen from the audience.

STAGE PROPERTIES

ACT ONE

> Ladder, against wall
> Small bucket
> Wooden sword, behind bush

ACT TWO

> Pompino pennant, on flagpole
> Box with will, in wall niche
> Stick or twig, for BURLY to write with
> Bath towel, behind bush

ACT THREE

> Dumbtop pennant, on pole
> Box with will, on ground
> Small bucket
> Wooden sword

HAND PROPERTIES

ACT ONE

> Battered felt hat, with band   PAPA
> Old-fashioned watch, on chain   "
> Folded paper, to fit in watch   "

Pompino pennant	PAPA
Colored balls *	"
Handkerchief	"
Umbrella	"
Odds and ends, in pocket of clown suit	"
Costume trunk, with all costumes but MARINA'S	FELIX and GUNDER
Gypsy costume	MARINA
Police whistle	BURLY
Picnic hamper, with sandwiches	JOHN and ERIC
Colored balls *	EACH BAMBINO

ACT TWO

Yellow pennant with red dragon	HUMPTY
Card, with notations	"
Colored balls *	"
King's robe and crown, from costume trunk	"
Boxing gloves	BURLY
Costume trunk	"
Helmet and spear, from costume trunk	"
Tools	"
Food hamper	"
Basket, with 3 chicken legs	AGNES
Folded paper	PAPA
Watch	"

ACT THREE

Handkerchief	WINNIE
Colored balls	"

---

* Balls can be made of cloth filled with cotton, of yarn covered with net, or cut from colored sponge or synthetic rubber. They must be soft to prevent bouncing and minimize rolling.

Ladder	WINNIE
Watch and folded paper	HUMPTY
Pencil	"
Pompino pennant	"

COSTUMES

PAPA POMPINO wears a nondescript, baggy suit and battered felt hat throughout, except in Act One, when he changes to a colorful clown suit with appropriate hat, shoes, gloves and, possibly, a false nose. He wears his felt hat on the back of his head which gives a very youthful appearance.

BURLY BINKOWITZ wears loud sports clothes in Act One. In Act Two he wears sweat shirt, shorts, ankle shoes and socks for boxing practice. During this act he adds a pair of long trousers and retains costume through Act Three.

AGNES wears a pastel maid's uniform with apron but no cap.

HUMPTY wears a good suit or very correct gentlemen's sports clothes which set him apart from the Bambinos. The clothes should not be "sissy."

The BAMBINOS wear everyday school clothes, blue jeans, corduroy pants, sweaters, jumper dresses, babushkas, baseball caps, etc.— whatever is currently popular. A variety of colors and types of garments can be selected. The costumes which they take from the trunk for their show need not be complete and no attempt need be made to conceal their everyday clothes.

King of Hearts (FELIX)	Long robe and crown
Queen of Hearts (WINNIE)	Long robe and crown
Knave of Hearts (JOHN)	Short robe
Jester (ERIC)	Headpiece, attached to shoulder cape or jacket, bells
Guard (GUNDER)	Viking helmet and spear
Medieval Lady (PAMELA)	Cape and tall peaked hat with veil
Dancer (MARINA)	Gypsy skirt and head scarf, tambourine
Chinese Lady (TSING LING)	Chinese robe and head piece

The Think Machine

A PLAY OF THE FUTURE

BY CHARLOTTE B. CHORPENNING

EDITORS' NOTE

The Think Machine is a science fiction play for a small cast interested in experimenting with new and provocative material. The play has to do with the unspoken thoughts of men and is bound to make for stimulating discussion. Since it presents no difficult production problems, an older group might enjoy working on it by themselves.

The words of the thoughts and the buzzing sounds, which reflect unworded emotions, present a fine problem in communication and one which will bring home the importance of speech. Finding the best means of conveying the thoughts to the audience will come from exprimentation. Disc or tape recordings can be used in this experimentation as an aid in perfecting the presentation.

The characters of Albert Royman, Sr., and Clyde Upton might be played by senior high school students. The play can easily be adapted to an all-male cast by changing Judy to a younger boy and the secretary to a male office worker.

The action of the play takes place on Lincoln's birthday. However, this does not in any way limit its use to that time of year.

THE THINK MACHINE
A Play of the Future

CHARACTERS

ALBERT ROYMAN, SR., *an inventor and scientist*
ALBERT ROYMAN, JR., *age 15, his son*
JUDY ROYMAN, *age 12, his daughter*
CLYDE UPTON, *a business genius*
MISS TAYLOR, *his secretary*

(Voice doubles for ROYMAN, SR., and UPTON)

PLACE: *An American city*
TIME: *A few years in the future*

SCENE ONE: *The Royman laboratory*
Late morning of February 12th

SCENE TWO: *Upton's office*
That afternoon

NOTE ON THE SETTINGS *

The laboratory in the Royman home of Scene One may be set on a curtain stage or in a simple box or screen set. Essentials are inside and outer doors, or openings, on opposite sides of the room, one further upstage than the other; a window, or opening treated as a window, center back; a table large enough for a newspaper to be spread out, and bench or stools; a smaller table at one side and a little back of the larger table, with bottles and

---

* Full production notes and a note to the director on handling the "thoughts" will be found at the end of the play.

some instruments used in precision work; against the opposite wall, a cabinet or filing case tall enough to bring the Lincoln picture on a level with Upton's eyes as he faces it.

The set for Scene Two, the study in the office wing of Upton's home, can have the same treatment. Essentials are a door, leading to the rest of the office; a window with window seat beneath it; a modern desk without drawers or table treated as a desk and a desk chair; a rug so placed that the report may be slipped under one corner in full view of the audience; Lincoln picture hung on wall. Since this is the study of a prosperous man, the set could be further dressed with a large globe of the world, table with magazines, stand with plant or vase of leaves, etc.

SCENE ONE

SCENE: *The Royman laboratory. Late morning.*

At the rise of the curtain ROYMAN *is standing by the small work table looking down at a small metal case, about the size of a man's watch, which is on a wooden block high enough to make inspection easy without bending uncomfortably low.* ALBERT *is standing near, watching with eager interest.*

ROYMAN. The end of ten year's work—

ALBERT (*indicating another small object on the long table*). Shall I bring the little gadget now?

ROYMAN. Better let me handle it, son. (*He picks up another object of a shape similar to the first, handling it with extreme care, almost reverence, and sets it in the case.*) Hand me the magnifier. Let me look at the cerebral-radar microantenna once more. (ALBERT *does.* ROYMAN *peers down into the case from several angles, nods and closes the lid.*) Just right—

ALBERT. Now can I help with the test? You've been so secret
about it I don't know what we've been making all this
time.

ROYMAN. We've been making the most important gadget
science has ever invented—

ALBERT. That little thing?

ROYMAN. Size isn't the last word, son.

ALBERT. More important than the atom bomb?

ROYMAN. Yes.

ALBERT. More important than spaceships when we get them?

ROYMAN. Yes! It may help us to know how to use those
things.

ALBERT. Jiminy! It scares me. I bet I know! You've been experimenting ever since I can remember with the things
that come to us through the air—like the way radio makes
us hear things and television makes us see things. And—
yes, sir!

ROYMAN. So what?

ALBERT. Lately you've gone crazy about that gadget that finds
out whether a person is dreaming— What do you call it?

ROYMAN. Electroencephalograph.

ALBERT. Yes. You've invented something to make you hear
the dreams! (ROYMAN *laughs to himself with pride over
the boy's keenness.*)

ROYMAN. You're on the beam, but it's a lot more than that
—if it works—

ALBERT. What are you going to call it?

ROYMAN. Electrocerebralographaudiotransformer.

ALBERT. Aw, Dad! Say it again.

ROYMAN (*breaking it into separate parts*). Electro—cerebral—
o—graph—audio—transformer.

ALBERT. That's a worse jaw-breaker than what you call the dream machine.

ROYMAN. Well, you and I will just call it the Think Machine.

ALBERT. I can't wait to try it!

ROYMAN. There's nothing to do now but wait till the solder sets.

ALBERT. Why don't you eat? You weren't at breakfast.

ROYMAN. Forgot all about it! I was up till daylight. The machine was so near ready I couldn't sleep till I finished. Guess I can snatch a bite while the solder cools. (*He turns back after starting to hurry off. Just as he does so* JUDY *enters with a framed picture of Lincoln, which she whips behind her back at sight of her father.*) Don't leave the lab alone, son. (JUDY *is smiling up at him, excitedly, as he turns again to leave.* ALBERT *shows concern about the picture.*)

JUDY. Happy holiday, Daddy!

ROYMAN. What?

JUDY. Have you *forgotten* this is Lincoln's birthday?!

ROYMAN. So it is. No holiday for me till I'm sure my last ten years' work wasn't for nothing. (JUDY *looks at* ALBERT *in questioning disappointment. He shakes his head.*)

JUDY. Oh-h—I thought you said you'd finish it today.

ALBERT. He did!

ROYMAN. If it works.

JUDY. When'll you know?

ROYMAN. Just as soon as I've had a bit of breakfast. (JUDY *laughs with pride.*)

JUDY. I saved some for you. I got breakfast all by myself this morning, to celebrate.

ROYMAN. Come along, then.

JUDY. I've got to tell Al a secret first. The fruit's on the table, and I kept your oatmeal hot. I'll fix the egg and toast by the time you're ready for them. (*She twists around so she can use one hand to open the door for him without showing the picture.* ROYMAN *goes off. Holding up the picture.*) I thought our surprise was to celebrate Dad's finishing his new invention today. He's forgotten it's Lincoln's birthday.

ALBERT. No use trying to celebrate till he knows the invention works. He'd just say, "Not now. Not now." (*He copies his father's impatient gesture.*)

JUDY (*setting the picture up on the cabinet*). The frame's just as good as if we'd bought it.

ALBERT. Of course! We do good work in the shop at school. It looks exactly like the one I saw in Mr. Upton's study. (*As they study the picture—*) Wouldn't Lincoln be surprised if he knew how many people are thinking of him today?

JUDY (*under the spell of it*). Ye-eah—it's as if—(*hunting for words*)—as if that night he was shot, his life wasn't done yet—and—and—all sorts of folks have to keep on living it for him— (*As they stand absorbed in the picture,* UPTON *passes the window and looks in.* ALBERT *glances from the picture to the Think Machine and back, interrupting his absorbed gaze with a start.*)

ALBERT. Say! You'd better scoot or Dad'll come back without his egg.

JUDY (*running to the door*). Don't you let him see the picture till I come.

ALBERT. 'Course not. You earned half the money for it, didn't you?

JUDY (*disappearing*). Hide it! (ALBERT *has his hands up to take down the picture when a brisk knock on the outside door is followed by* UPTON's *opening it.* ALBERT *turns to him quickly.*)

UPTON. Good morning!

ALBERT. Oh! Mr. Upton. Come in.

UPTON. Whew! It's hot in here. Don't you know the weather is celebrating Lincoln's birthday? It's like spring out! (*As* ALBERT *sets the windows a little ajar—*) Is your father in?

ALBERT. He's at breakfast.

UPTON (*with a glance at the clock*). Breakfast? I'll wait. Oh—a Lincoln—just like mine!

ALBERT. It's a present for Dad. Ever since you talked to me about Lincoln in your office, I've got to feeling about Lincoln the way you do.

UPTON. Good! (*Offering his hand, they shake on it.*) He's been the inspiration of my life since I was your age.

ALBERT. Yes, sir, I know. (*After a quick glance at the Think Machine.*) I'll get Dad. Of course you'll stay till I come back. Dad never leaves the lab alone.

UPTON (*sitting down by the table*). Sure. Got a morning paper? I missed mine today.

ALBERT (*handing him an unopened one from the table*). We haven't even opened it. I'll be right back. (*Exits.* UPTON *unfolds paper, and stares at the headline in great excitement.*)

UPTON (*reading aloud*). "New science wonder gadget." Royman's new invention! "We learn on good authority that the Royman laboratory makes a final test on a new wonder machine today—" (*His voice fades as he rapidly scans the rest of the article. He throws down the paper, other side up, straightens up and snaps his fingers.*) I'll get that gadget into my own hands or my name's not Clyde Upton. (*He *whirls in excitement and comes face to face with the Lincoln picture.)* You were a poor boy and you got to be the biggest man in the United States. I was a poor boy and I'll be the biggest man in the whole world! Everyone in this country looks up to you. Everyone in the whole world will look up to me when I'm through with this gadget. *(The sound of the turning of the doorknob recalls him to himself. He turns to* ALBERT *quietly, as he enters.)*

ALBERT. I'm sorry, Mr. Upton, but Father's busy. He can't see anyone right now.

UPTON. I see by the paper that there may be news today. Some of the directors of the Royman Laboratories promised to let me seen the records as soon as there was anything sure. I'll drop over again in a little while. I want a word with your father.

ALBERT. I'll tell him.

UPTON *(leaving with a wave of his hand).* Good-bye. *(*ALBERT *sees* UPTON *to the door, closes it and goes back to table, hears* JUDY's *voice off and hastily hides the Lincoln behind the cabinet.)*

JUDY *(off).* Daddy! You don't hear a thing I say.

ROYMAN *(entering with a little laugh).* I've something on my mind, just now. *(He goes to the Think Machine and stands looking down on it in intense stillness.)*

JUDY *(noticing her father's deep excitement).* What's the matter, Daddy?

ALBERT *(a finger on her lips).* Sh-h— He's afraid it won't work. *(*ROYMAN *nods and smiles at* ALBERT, *pleased with his understanding, and takes up the Think Machine.)*

JUDY. What's that?

ROYMAN. It's a great secret, Judy.

JUDY *(offering her ear for a whisper).* Goody! I like secrets.

ROYMAN (*smiling*). I can't tell anyone till I know it works. Run along now.

JUDY. But, Daddy, I have to wait because—

ROYMAN. Not now, Not now. Run along. I must try it out. You and Mother shall be the first to know when it's time to tell. (JUDY *runs out, mollified.*)

ALBERT. Dad, did you mean that little thing will let us hear—thoughts?

ROYMAN (*fastening a strap onto the machine*). You sit down there and I'll tell you exactly what you are thinking.

ALBERT. How'll you know?

ROYMAN. I'll hear you.

ALBERT. Huh? That'll let you hear me think, the way radio and television let us hear people talk?

ROYMAN. It will if it works. (*Breathless with excitement.*) We're going to find out—now.

ALBERT. Will I hear what I think, too?

ROYMAN. No. You have to have this part of the machine against your skin to hear. But you will know your own thoughts, and can tell me whether I am right.

ALBERT (*squirming at the idea*). Gee, Dad. I— Hold on a minute— I'll get Judy for you. She won't mind.

ROYMAN. Wait, now. (*Amused.*) You're not ashamed of your thoughts, are you?

ALBERT. No—only—it's sort of like taking off your clothes in public. You don't say out everything you think.

ROYMAN. You have something there, son! Well, we'll turn the tables. I'll put it on you. You shall hear my thoughts. Hold out your arm.

ALBERT (*holding out his arm*). Gee, that'll be great! Will I see what you see in your mind, too?

ROYMAN (*fastening the machine on ALBERT's wrist as he talks*).

No. You know the air is full of waves. Sound is one kind. Light is another kind. It's true we don't always think in words. But words are the only kind of thinking I can handle on this machine. I'll work on what we see as we think, next. I'll get the pictures some day. There! Now, we'll find out. (ROYMAN *steps back as he finishes. He takes a long breath, scarcely able to stand still in his excitement.*)

ALBERT. I don't hear a thing.

ROYMAN. You have to turn the little knob first. See it?

ALBERT (*turning his wrist this way and that toward the audience, and touching the dial with one finger*). Just like turning on the radio—or television!

ROYMAN. Don't turn it on till I give you the signal. (*Picking up the stop watch.*) I want to time how long it takes for the sound to come clear. Say, "Time" as soon as you hear anything—if you do. (*Excited tableau, ROYMAN's hand up ready for the signal, ALBERT's fingers on the dial, his eyes on ROYMAN. ROYMAN drops his hand, his eyes still on the stop watch.*) Now! (ALBERT *starts as a low buzz comes to his ears, and lifts his hand ready to speak, but is absorbed by what he hears. It is his father's voice, but very fast and broken into phrases, highly colored with feeling and excitement, and interrupted by emotional buzz of thought not taking the form of words. The thoughts, in words or otherwise, are enclosed in brackets.*) [Bz-z-z-z— Boy right— z-z- afraid to face test—z-z-z-z—call me fool—trusting own son—only fifteen—z-z-z-z—smart—z-z—true blue—never let his dad down way I did mine—that night I lost a letter —z-z-z—valuable letter—z-z-z—he sent me to mail it—I never told him—z-z—I lost it—z-z-z-z-z-! Watch out! Machine!—Not this quick—z-z-z-z-z—dark night—z-z—

me just fifteen, like him—z-z-z-z-z-z-z-z-z- Time getting
long—z-z-z-z— Not going to work?]

ALBERT (*startled to realize he's been listening without giving
the signal*). It does, Dad!

ROYMAN. Works? [Z-z-z-z-z-z-z-!]

ALBERT. I heard you thinking!

ROYMAN. It works!!—[Z-z-z-z- Thinking! What thinking?
Own son—z-z—!] It works! The greatest gift of science!
The good that can come of it! Think of it, son.—If men—
all of us—really understand each other! There's some good
in everyone—if we know how to get it going— [Z-z-z-z
—great discovery—I did it—I—fame—fortune—z-z—]
(ALBERT's *gasp of surprise suddenly reminds* ROYMAN. *He
is startled at his own thoughts and leaps to turn off the
dial.*) [Z-Z-Z-Z-Z-Z-!!!] Take it off!

ALBERT (*doing so*). I—I didn't mean to spy on you— I—I—

ROYMAN. You were right, son. You don't say out everything
you think. You don't even know it yourself, half the time.
(*Both laugh.*)

ALBERT. Did you ever find that important letter, Dad?

ROYMAN. No. I didn't try very hard, and never told my father
I lost it. I'm still ashamed of that. I know you'd never
fail me like that, son. (*Proud of him.*) Now I must find
someone else to try it on.

ALBERT. I know who! Mr. Upton—he's coming back.

ROYMAN (*alert*). Upton? What did he want?

ALBERT. He wanted to know how the experiment was coming.

ROYMAN (*quickly*). What did you tell him?

ALBERT. I wanted you to finish your breakfast, so I said you
couldn't see him just then. He's coming back. He was
real excited. He'll be here any minute. (*Both look up at
the clock.* UPTON *comes to the window, smiling, widening*

the opening a little, ready to hail them, but stops short at ROYMAN's *words. He steps back, but is clearly listening.*)

ROYMAN. Clyde Upton. He's the last man I'd let in on this till I'm sure I can control how it's used.

ALBERT. I thought Mr. Upton was a friend of yours.

ROYMAN. Well—yes.

ALBERT. He's interested in science and your inventions.

ROYMAN. Too interested. (UPTON's *face is very expressive at this and the following.*)

ALBERT. You always said he was such a fine man.

ROYMAN. In most ways—yes. He's brilliant—self-made— started as a poor boy.

ALBERT. I don't understand you, Dad. Why, he's talked to me about Lincoln and—well, I think he's great.

ROYMAN. He might have been—but he wants too much to get everything in his own hands. There's no telling what use he'd make of this little miracle—I just begin to see the dangers.

ALBERT. It does seem kind of sneaky—listening in on a person who doesn't know it.

ROYMAN. I never thought of it that way— (*He is startled. Looking at the machine in his hand, begins to move this way and that, restless, thinking out loud, thus crossing and recrossing the vision of* UPTON *whose peering face vanishes and reappears as* ROYMAN *passes and repasses.* UPTON's *expressions vary: superior smiles, anger, and sly determination.*) Such a triumph of science! The good that might come of it—working together— Peace— No man is all bad. (*Apprehensive.*) No man is all good, either. This could be used— No, Upton mustn't know about it yet. (*Puts machine on table.*)

ALBERT. He does know, Dad. He saw it in the paper this morning.

ROYMAN. It's much too early for newspaper stories! Upton knows the sort of thing our group is working on, of course. He's put up the money for some of it. But I'm the only one in the world with all the know-how for putting this machine together. I've worked alone on a lot of it.

ALBERT. He said some of the group promised to let him see the report when the invention had been tried out.

ROYMAN. I'm afraid some of them did. Too bad. I'll have to work out how to handle that before I see him.

ALBERT. I thought he'd be here by now. Guess he isn't coming.

ROYMAN (opening cabinet, takes out a large report and a small sheaf of notes). You stay here and make sure. I'll go to my study and think this out. Then I'll telephone some of the others. If he comes, tell him I'm tied up and can't be disturbed, and give him one of these. (Handing ALBERT the rather thick report.) Wait—I'll sign it. (Takes pen from pocket and signs.) Tell him that's all that's available yet.

ALBERT. What is it? (UPTON cranes his neck in to see.)

ROYMAN. A report of every experiment up to the time I began working alone—ten years ago.

ALBERT. Do you mean the part I've helped with isn't here?

ROYMAN. That's right. (Holding up the small sheets, fastened together.) These are my notes on the last stage of the invention. Here is the secret of it.

ALBERT. Gosh, Dad!

ROYMAN. Clyde Upton mustn't get his hands on this. I haven't even a copy yet. (UPTON watches cautiously, but steadily. Takes measure of small report with his hands as ROYMAN *holds it up, then starts to put it in his pocket.*)

ALBERT. Can't I see it, Dad? I know I won't understand all the mathematics and stuff, but there's a lot I helped in.

ROYMAN (*proud of him*). You understand a great deal for a boy of your age. Guess it's coming to you. How to work a miracle! (*Handing* ALBERT *his own report.*) See what you can make of it.

ALBERT (*fervently, seizing it eagerly, laying the other one on the table*). Thanks, Dad. (ROYMAN *puts the Think Machine in the cabinet.*)

ROYMAN. Keep your ears open for Upton. Put that in the cabinet with the Think Machine if he rings—or knocks. He's apt to come straight to the laboratory. I'm trusting you with the most important thing in my life, son. (AL- BERT *stands straight and salutes. Both laugh.*) I'll see Upton at the Directors' meeting this afternoon. He's invited. (*On his way out—*) Watch your thoughts if he comes. They show in your face.

ALBERT. By Jiminy, that's so! Yours did. But I wouldn't have known what they were if I hadn't heard them.

ROYMAN. You can learn. Upton reads faces like a book. (*Exit* ROYMAN. ALBERT *goes to the window to look for* UPTON, *who ducks out of sight as* ALBERT *comes and appears again as he returns to the table. As* ALBERT *sits at the table, poring over the small report,* UPTON *moves back a little, cautiously unzips his briefcase ready for quick use, and disappears toward the outer door.* ALBERT *is startled by* UPTON's *voice as he opens the door, speaking softly. The* BOY *draws the newspaper over the reports, the edge of the larger one showing.*)

UPTON. May I come in? Or are you still not to be interrupted?

ALBERT (*doing his best to "put on an act"*). Come right in, Mr. Upton. Sorry. Dad isn't here.

UPTON (*spotting the paper where the report was*). Is the great experiment all over?

ALBERT. Uh—something came up. Dad's in his study thinking it out. He said not to interrupt him.

UPTON (*edging toward the paper*). The paper spoke as if it would soon be announced.

ALBERT (*hastily*). Father says not to pay attention to the newspaper. It isn't time to publish anything.

UPTON (*watching* ALBERT'S *uneasiness with covert amusement*). No report for me, then?

ALBERT. Dad said to give you this. It's up to the time he began working alone. (UPTON *manages to drop the report as* ALBERT *hands it to him, so the sheets spread over the floor.*)

ALBERT. Sorry. It isn't bound yet.

UPTON. My fault. (*As* ALBERT *stoops to gather them up,* UPTON *slips the other smaller report from under the newspaper and into his briefcase.*)

ALBERT (*getting the sheets into order*). He signed this for you.

UPTON (*reading*). "Compliments of Albert Royman, Senior." That's good of him. Tell him I appreciate his confidence.

ALBERT. I will, sir. He said he'd see you at the meeting this afternoon.

UPTON. I'll read this immediately and be back by—four o'clock. I hope to thank him in person, then. (*He slips it into his briefcase, zips it shut, goes briskly out the door, and past the window.*)

ALBERT. Whew! He sure is in a rush. He kept eyeing me— (*He is about to lift the newspaper when* JUDY *bounces in.*)

JUDY. Hi! What makes you jump like that?

ALBERT (*with a quick look at the paper*). I—I didn't hear you coming.

JUDY. You've got another secret!

ALBERT. Me?

JUDY. You needn't try to put on. I can see it in your face.

ALBERT (*trying for a "dead pan"*). What do you see in my face?

JUDY. Just—you're trying to keep something to yourself. (ALBERT's *eyes turn toward the newspaper.*)

ALBERT. You don't know what it is, though!

JUDY. Yes I do! It's about the newspaper. You keep looking at it, quick and sly. (*She runs to pick it up.* ALBERT *leaps to stop her.*)

ALBERT. Let it alone!

JUDY. There aren't any secrets in a newspaper. You've hidden something under it. (*She darts behind him to snatch up the paper. He gets in her way, she dodges around in circles, snatches it and holds it over his head.*) I beat! (*Turning to see what is under it, lets it drop.*) You fooled me. (ALBERT *stares at the empty space, seizes the newspaper, shakes it, horror-struck.*) What's eating you?

ALBERT. It's gone! I gave him the two at once! I've got to get it.

JUDY. Get what?

ALBERT. Mr. Upton has the wrong report—the one Dad didn't want him to have. I'm going for it.

JUDY (*helpful*). I'll tell Daddy.

ALBERT. No!! Don't disturb him. I've got to get it back at once.

JUDY (*with enthusiasm*). So Daddy'll never know you lost it!

ALBERT. Yes! He trusted me. Don't say a word to anyone till I come back.

JUDY. Now, I've got a secret! (ALBERT *swiftly shuts and locks the windows, checks the doors to the cabinet, then on second thought opens it and slips the Think Machine into his pocket.*)

JUDY. What're you taking?

ALBERT. Never mind.

JUDY. I know! Daddy's secret! I'm coming, too!

ALBERT. You can't go into Mr. Upton's house. Things might happen.

JUDY. I'll wait for you outside then. (*With great relish.*) It's a mystery! Like on television!

CURTAIN

SCENE TWO

SCENE: *Upton's office. That afternoon.*

UPTON *stands by the desk in high excitement and triumph, opens briefcase, takes out the two reports, throws the larger one on the desk, and settles down to reading the smaller one avidly, turning the pages fast, with sounds of delight. The doorbell rings, but he is too absorbed to notice it. After a few pages, the striking of the clock startles him.*

UPTON (*murmuring*). Photostat—quick— (*He pushes the buzzer on his desk.* MISS TAYLOR *enters.*)

TAYLOR. Yes, sir?

UPTON. Please get ready to make some photostats right away. We must have copies of this at once.

TAYLOR. We're out of sensitized paper, Mr. Upton.

UPTON. There's plenty more in the storeroom. Just hunt until you find it. And (*handing her the large report*) file this in the Royman folder.

TAYLOR (*going*). Yes, sir.

UPTON. And no visitors. I'm busy. (*He snatches up the small report eagerly. At first he does not heed* ALBERT's *voice, off.*)

ALBERT (*off*). Are you Mr. Upton's secretary?

TAYLOR (*off*). I am. May I help you?

ALBERT (*off*). I'm Albert Royman. I want to see Mr. Upton. (*At the name,* UPTON *shifts in his chair to hear better.*)

TAYLOR (*off*). Mr. Upton is busy. Will you leave a message?

ALBERT (*off*). I have to see him myself, right away.

TAYLOR (*off*). I'm sorry. Mr. Upton is seeing no one.

ALBERT (*off*). He'll see me. He's my father's friend. He just came from our house. I have to get something from him. Please tell him I'm here. (UPTON *lifts a startled head.*)

TAYLOR (*off*). I'm sorry. I have strict orders. (UPTON *snatches up the report, looks around for a place to hide it. He starts to put it in the briefcase, shakes his head, looks around quickly.*)

ALBERT (*off*). I have to see him.

TAYLOR (*off*). You'll have to come back later.

ALBERT (*off*). I can't wait till later. There's been a mistake. I gave him the wrong report. I must take it back before my father needs it.

TAYLOR (*off*). Not now. Good afternoon. (UPTON *spots a place to hide the report and tucks it behind the picture of Lincoln.*)

ALBERT (*off*). I don't want to be rude, but I'm going in there.

TAYLOR (*off, very firm*). No, please. (UPTON *backs away from*

*the picture, making sure the report does not show, hurries
to the office door, opens it.)*

UPTON (*cheerily*). Do I hear Albert Royman's voice?

ALBERT (*entering*). Yes, sir. She wouldn't let me in.

UPTON. She's just obeying orders. It's all right, Miss Taylor.
You didn't know this young man was a special case. Go
ahead to the storeroom. (*Laying a hand on* ALBERT's
shoulder.) Come in, my boy. Albert Royman's son is always welcome. (ALBERT *beams with relief.*)

ALBERT. Thank you, sir. Father left one report for you. I gave
you another by mistake. I came to get that one. He needs
it right away.

UPTON. You're mistaken, young man. Mine has your father's
signature. You said the last one wasn't ready.

ALBERT. I know. But it was on the table. I must have picked
it up with the one I gave you. Because when I looked for
it, it was gone. (*Desperate.*) You must have it. If you
haven't, it's lost. Dad will never trust me again. Besides—
we were the only ones in the room from the time it was
there to the time it wasn't. You must have taken it along
by mistake. Please think, Mr. Upton.

UPTON. I am thinking, my boy. I see that room and the newspaper on the table, and you lifting the end of the paper
to draw out the report and give it to me. (ALBERT *turns
away to hide his struggle to keep back tears, leans against
wall under Lincoln picture, in despair.*) You don't suppose
I'd think one thing and say another, do you?

ALBERT. No. Only— (ALBERT *lifts his head, his face working
with the shock of what* UPTON's *last words suggest. He
casts a furtive glance at* UPTON *and slips the Think Machine out of his pocket. He turns his back to* UPTON *and
manages to fasten the machine onto his wrist. He can't*

help a start as a buzz of sounds clears into contemptuous words.) Of course not, Mr. Upton—only— Where did it go?

UPTON. [Z-z-z-z-z- Anyone but—dumbbell—z-z—know I took it.] (*Notes* ALBERT's *start.*) What's the matter?

ALBERT. Just—the more I think, the surer I am it must be here. (UPTON *straightens with a flash of temper.*)

UPTON. [Z-z-z-z-z-!] (*Sharp.*) Now see here, young man! [Z-z-z- Watch step!— Keep him—z-z-z-] (*He breaks off with a laugh.*) You almost touched my temper, lad. [Get rid of him. Z-z-z- Give him an out.] You surely don't think your father's friend would try to deceive you? Look me in the eye. (ALBERT *forces himself to meet* UPTON's *steady gaze. Horrified conviction sweeps his face as he realizes that his father's mistrust of* UPTON *was well founded. It is followed by a wave of despair as he loses hope of getting the report. He slumps again, back to* UPTON, *but lifts his head cautiously, listening.* UPTON *watches him with a smile of contempt.*) [Good joke z-z- right here z-z-z- breaking heart over it z-z-z-! Don't get soft! Got to have report z-z-z kid putty in my hands z-z-z-z work him—] (*Kindly.*) Look here, lad. You'd better run home and look around again. You're never going to find your father's report here. (ALBERT *turns in time to see* UPTON's *eyes.*) [Z-z-z-z-z- Rid of him. Photostat it—take it back—say just found—]

ALBERT (*beginning to play his own game*). Where is it, then? May I see what I gave you, before I go?

UPTON. It's been filed.

ALBERT. Here?

UPTON (*going to office door, opens it, with an amiable smile*). [Z-z-z- What up to?] In the file room. Miss Taylor—that report I gave you to file just now. . . . Miss Taylor!

ALBERT. You sent her to the storeroom, Mr. Upton.

UPTON. Oh, yes. She'll be back soon.

ALBERT. I want to get home, and look, like you said, Mr. Upton. Don't you know where she put it?

UPTON. Skip home and come back if you don't find it there. [Z-z-z- Photostat—won't take long.]

ALBERT. I guess you'll think I'm cracked, Mr. Upton, but I can't get over thinking the two of them must be together. (*Sits, window seat.*) No use going home till I've seen.

UPTON (*genial*). All right, Albert. [Z-z-z- Safe to leave him— z-z- never enter head to look—z-z-z-] (*Going.*) Make yourself easy. I'll be right back. (*His gay whistle fades in the distance after he shuts the door.* ALBERT *opens window, leans out, reaching down.*)

ALBERT (*softly*). Judy! Sh-h-h—! Climb up. (JUDY's *face appears, glowing with adventure.*)

JUDY (*whispering*). What's up?

ALBERT. Sh-h-h—! (*He helps her onto the window sill and into the room.*) Don't make any noise. We've got to search this room for Dad's report. Hurry and help me. (JUDY *begins with gusto, looks under window seat cushion, shakes draperies, etc., while* ALBERT *looks in briefcase, around desk, etc. As they cover all likely places,* ALBERT *becomes more desperate and* JUDY *takes alarm from his tension.*)

JUDY. That report isn't anywhere.

ALBERT. It has to be. I know it's here.

JUDY. How do you know?

ALBERT. I just know—never mind. Hurry, Judy! Hunt some more.

JUDY. There's no place else to look. (*Glancing around, spots the Lincoln picture.*) Oh, there's the picture just like ours.

ALBERT. That's it! He's just mean enough to hide it there. (*Darts to picture, pulls out report, leaving picture a bit crooked.*) Here it is! (*Looks apprehensively toward door.*) Now scoot!

JUDY. Something's awful wrong . . . it's scary. (UPTON'S *whistle, off.*)

ALBERT (*almost pushing her toward window*). Hurry, Judy!

JUDY (*with conviction*). I think you're in danger!

ALBERT. Cut it out. I'm all right. There you go. (JUDY, *obviously unconvinced, climbs through window, watches AL-BERT for a moment before disappearing with a look of determination on her face.* ALBERT *had started to unbutton his jacket to put the report under it, but, changing his mind, slips it under corner of the rug, then dashes to sit on window seat.* UPTON *enters, the signed report in his hand. He lays it on the desk.*)

UPTON. [Z-z-z— Sitting same place—!] Here's what you gave me. "Compliments of Albert Royman, Senior." (ALBERT *crosses and stares at it, looks down at the rug, hesitates.*)

ALBERT. I—I thought there were two.

UPTON. You see, it must still be at home. (ALBERT *turns away, gets an idea.*)

ALBERT. Well, I don't see how it could be. But if it isn't here, it has to be there, hasn't it?

UPTON. [Z-z-z-! What's the boy up to? Z-z-z- No good at putting on.] Looks like it, doesn't it?

ALBERT. Are you sure it wasn't in the file with this one?— And you just didn't notice it?

UPTON [Z-z-z-z— Trying to get rid of me again?] (*His eyes go to the picture.*) [Crooked! Z-Z-Z-Z-!!] You may go and look in the file yourself, if you doubt my word.

ALBERT (*looking down at rug uneasily*). Oh, no, sir— No!

UPTON. I see my picture isn't quite straight. That'll never do for Lincoln, will it? (UPTON goes, as if casually, to straighten it, feeling behind for the report as he does so. There is a blaze of fury as he finds the report gone, but this fades to keenness and caution.) [Z-Z-Z-! Z-z- Steady. Z-z- Get it back—] Now see here, my lad. Don't try to fool Clyde Upton. There were some papers behind that picture for safe-keeping. You thought they were the report you're looking for. (ALBERT is flustered and turns away.) They're not. Give them back.

ALBERT. I haven't got them.

UPTON. Where have you hidden them? (Looking hard at ALBERT.) Under your coat! (ALBERT says nothing, stalling for time.) Are you going to give them to me, or shall I take them?

ALBERT (defiantly). I dare you! (UPTON comes toward him. ALBERT dodges about. UPTON catches him, they wrestle and ALBERT goes down. UPTON searches him, finally gets to his feet, unsuccessful.) I told you I didn't have it. (Rising.) How did you expect to get what I didn't have? (ALBERT stretches to straighten his coat, thus exposing his wrist beyond the edge of his sleeve. UPTON spots the Think Machine.)

UPTON. [Z-Z-! No watch —Z-z-! Royman gadget! By George!] (He leaps to snatch ALBERT's arm.) What's this? (UPTON throws ALBERT and, with a knee on ALBERT's arm, unfastens the machine, puts it on his own wrist as he moves away.)

ALBERT. Let it be! (ALBERT scrambles to his feet, ready to fight.) Give it here! It's Dad's! (UPTON holds up his arm with the machine on his wrist.)

UPTON. Steady, young man. If you make trouble I'll smash this thing on the edge of the desk here. You don't want to throw away ten years of your father's experiments, do you? (ALBERT *makes a despairing gesture of protest and stands quiet.* UPTON *lowers his wrist and stares at the machine.*) How does it work? Do you have to wind it? Answer. (ALBERT *straightens with a faint smile.*)

ALBERT. I won't. (UPTON *lifts his wrist to carry out his threat in a flash of fury.*) No!!! (ALBERT *starts to seize the arm, halts himself, sinks into a chair by the desk in despair. The door opens.* ROYMAN, *followed by* JUDY, *enters.* ALBERT *looks up, jumps to his feet.*) Dad! He's got the Think Machine!

UPTON (*pulling himself together, hastily unfastening gadget from his wrist*). Certainly, why not? The boy brought it here to show me. Here it is. (*Handing it to* ROYMAN, *who takes it and turns to* ALBERT, *questioning.*)

ALBERT. I did bring it here, but not to show to Mr. Upton.

ROYMAN. Then why did you bring it?

ALBERT. I thought I might need it. Dad, I gave him your secret report by mistake. I came to get it back.

UPTON. That's right. But I didn't have that report. Albert must have lost it.

ALBERT. I didn't, Dad. (*Quickly stoops and gets report from under the rug, hands it to his father.*)

ROYMAN (*taking it*). How did this get under your rug, Upton?

UPTON. I know nothing about it. (ROYMAN, *turning from* UPTON, *appears to be checking report but is actually holding the Think Machine to his wrist.*) The boy must have put it there himself. He could have. I was out of my office. [Z-z-z-z— Everything's all right.—z-z-z— Royman's angry at boy—z-z-z—never suspect me.—Z-z-z—!] Well, the report and the new invention are both safe. (*Looking at his watch.*) Ought we not to be getting to the board meeting?

ROYMAN (*with a look at* ALBERT, *who has been studying his father's expression as he listened to* UPTON's *thoughts*). The Think Machine is successful and safe—thanks to you, my boy. (*Putting his hand on* ALBERT's *shoulder.*)

ALBERT (*beaming*). Thanks, Dad. (*With meaning.*) I tried it out on Mr. Upton before you came. I heard his thoughts.

ROYMAN (*as* UPTON *looks from one to the other and at the gadget, confused and startled*). Good boy. You can tell me all about it later. Come, Upton, we have a great deal to discuss before the board meeting. (*They start out—*UPTON *hesitantly.* JUDY *runs to* ALBERT, *who is standing beside the Lincoln picture.*)

JUDY. After the board meeting, we'll give Daddy our picture.

ALBERT. We'll celebrate the Think Machine and Lincoln together!

CURTAIN

NOTE TO THE DIRECTOR

The following is suggested as the way in which the thoughts of the characters can be conveyed to the audience. Royman, Sr., and Upton can have doubles, who, from off-stage, are responsible for both the thought words and the "z-z-z" sounds. The thoughts can be projected by the natural voice alone or over a public address system. With this as a basis, variations can be tried. For example, if no public address system is used, experiments can be made with the actor on stage carrying the "z-z-z" sounds, since the Z sound does not require moving the lips. Thus the double would give only the words of the thoughts. This is more taxing in regard to timing but may prove more interesting and satisfactory to some young players. If a public address system is used, experiments can be made to achieve the best effect, i.e., full voice with low volume, soft voice with higher volume, etc. Care should be taken that the thoughts are clearly heard by the audience.

The double must be able to see and follow the movements of his opposite number on stage, since good teamwork in timing is essential. Each double must understand the character as thoroughly as the actor on stage and become sensitive to the actor's manner and the way he would convey the thoughts were he actually doing it. Disc or tape recordings of the thought words and "z-z-z" sounds, made by the on-stage actors and by the doubles, also, would be helpful in developing the parts. A comparison of tempos, inflections, etc., would lead to a harmonious blending of the work of the actors and their doubles.

The actors must realize that in the thought process there are many flashes too fast to be put into words and that often emotions are not translated into words. The "z-z-z" sounds of the unworded thoughts and feelings must vary in pitch, pace and volume according to the quality of the feeling aroused by the situation. To indicate this in the text would make difficult reading. Moreover, it would deny the actor the creative opportunity to work it out for himself. For example, on the first thoughts heard the "z-z-z" rises to clearness as quiet realization of Albert's part in the experiment comes to Royman. It changes little till at "fifteen" his pride in Albert swells it and lowers both pitch and volume. A sharp jump of caution before "watch out!" changes to reassurance after "not this quick." It fades into low-pitched memory, colored by pictures of the dark night and his misdemeanor. This is cut by sharp apprehension at "time's getting long." At Albert's interruption, hope of success crowds out everything. Then "heard you thinking" gives him a flash of fear. Then overwhelming joy in the success of his project fills the "z-z-z" with wonder and delight and his ego pipes up with personal pride until Albert's stare shocks him into realization and the "z-z-z" rises almost to a scream.

Most young actors will enjoy working out their own patterns for the "z-z-z" sounds. When help is needed, the director can suggest a discussion of words the characters would use in places where only sound comes through.

Since many thoughts take the form of mental pictures, as is indicated in the play, the director can interest young people fond of drawing and painting in putting the "z-z-z" sounds into pictures. If this activity is done during the development of the play, an exhibit can be hung for the audience to see before and after performances.

PRODUCTION NOTES

STAGE PROPERTIES

SCENE ONE

Filing cabinet or chest
Large table
Smaller table (bottles, instruments)
Bench or stools at table
Clock
Chairs—optional

SCENE TWO

Desk, or table treated as desk
Buzzer on desk
Desk chair
Window seat
Rug
Clock
Framed picture of Lincoln (should have pocket on back so papers will not slip out accidentally)

In adding anything to this set care should be taken that there are not too many articles where UPTON could easily hide the report, thus prolonging the search of Albert and Judy. Chairs, a standing world globe, table with magazines, plant or piece of sculpture would all be appropriate. Pictures, aside from the Lincoln, should not be used, but maps applied as part of the paneling of the study would be decorative.

HAND PROPERTIES

SCENE ONE

Case for machine	On small table
Wrist strap for Machine case	" " "
Think Machine	On large table
Magnifier	" " "

Stop watch (need not be genuine)	On large table
Newspaper	" " "
Large report	In cabinet
Small report	" "
Fountain pen	ROYMAN, SR.
Lincoln picture (probably smaller than one used in Scene Two, but picture and frame design should be identical)	JUDY
Briefcase	UPTON

SCENE TWO

Briefcase	UPTON
Small report, large report	"
Think Machine	ALBERT

COSTUMES

All costumes are what is current when the play is given.

ROYMAN wears a laboratory coat over shirt and trousers in Scene One and a business suit in Scene Two.

UPTON's dress shows him to be a very prosperous businessman. In Scene One, for his first entrance, he could carry a top coat over his arm.

ALBERT is informally but neatly dressed, like any school boy.

JUDY is neat and attractive in whatever is becoming for everyday wear. In Scene Two a cardigan sweater can be added.

MISS TAYLOR wears a suit or tailored dress.

SOUND

SCENE TWO

 Buzzer

 Doorbell

 Clock striking

ABOUT THE AUTHORS

CHARLOTTE (BARROWS) CHORPENNING (*The Think Machine*) grew up in a large family. Her father was a clergyman, later a university professor, and her mother, a musician. Some of their children were talented musically and Charlotte loved painting. The frequent shows given for family entertainment were dramatic, artistic and often accompanied by original or classical and folk music. After her marriage, Mrs. Chorpenning began to write, her first short story and some poetry being published. Her husband urged her to turn to playwriting and to study with Professor Baker at the Harvard 47 Workshop. She completed two years of work with Professor Baker, doing her first directing at Harvard. Her husband's death occurred at that time and she went to teach literature at Winona State Teachers' College in Minnesota, where she became engrossed in a number of community drama projects. From there she was called to join the staff of the Recreation Training School at Hull House in Chicago. It was while supervising the work of her students in settlements, churches and public recreation centers that she came to a full realization of the vividness of children's imaginations and the importance of plays for children as a social force. The Recreation Training School was later absorbed by Northwestern University, Mrs. Chorpenning then becoming a member of the Northwestern faculty. In the University she came to know Winifred Ward, who was organizing the Evanston Children's Theatre. Mrs. Chorpenning's first play, *The Emperor's New Clothes*, was written for this theatre. Dr. Maurice Gnesin of the Goodman Memorial Theatre of Chicago saw the production and invited Mrs. Chorpenning to become director of Children's

Theatre for the Goodman, a post from which she has just retired. There she had, for a number of years, a staff of research assistants to study the reactions of children's audiences. The plays which she wrote and directed for this theatre form the backbone of the published children's theatre literature in this country. Mrs. Chorpenning attributes the renown of the Goodman Children's Theatre to the excellent facilities, the brilliant designing and production, and the staff of the School of the Theatre which is part of the Art Institute of Chicago. Those who know her cannot fail to acknowledge also the hard work, the insight and the touch of genius that is "Chorpy."

MARGARET ELLEN CLIFFORD (*The Secret of the Worn-out Shoes*) confesses that at the age of ten she was coercing younger children to appear in plays of her direction. Her formal theatre training was received at Vassar, under Hallie Flanagan, and at the Gloucester School of the Little Theatre, topped off with a master's degree from the University of Chicago. An expedition to Russia, under Mrs. Flanagan's guidance, introduced her to the high quality that children's theatre could attain. A taste of professional theatre as an actress on Broadway and in summer stock led her back to her two constant interests, children's theatre and teaching. She has taught and directed at leading private schools, a public junior high school and in college and university departments. In her home town of Portland, Maine, she helped to found its children's theatre and served as director for a number of seasons. The war inspired the organization of a summer Trailer Theatre to play to young children in parks and at the housing projects, Miss Clifford acting as director for casts and crews of teen-agers. For three years she was dramatic supervisor for the Recreation Department of Peoria, Illinois, where she introduced creative dramatics and teen-age theatre in community centers. Her first play, *The Sleeping Beauty*, written at Vassar, was published and has been a perennial favorite. Several adaptations and originals were written to meet the exacting demands of the Trailer Theatre. *The Secret of the Worn-out Shoes* was first produced by the Portland Community Children's Theatre in collaboration with the Dorothy Mason School of the Dance, using a cast ranging from ten to fifteen years of age, the author directing the production.

MARTHA BENNETT KING (*Papa Pompino and the Prizefighter*) has had three interwoven careers, as wife and mother, businesswoman and artist. She describes herself as a complete mid-westerner: born in Wisconsin and educated at the University of Chicago with graduate work there and at Northwestern. Marriage and babies interrupted a career as a concert singer, but with sons grown she has found a new music field, is playing her own guitar and singing folk songs to groups of children and adults; and has recorded *Sing Me to Sleep* songs (several originals) by Marty, and the series, *Adventures in Folk Song*. For several years she was Children's Book Editor for the *Chicago Sun and Sun-Times*. She has held posts of director of an International Library for Children in Chicago and university lecturer in children's literature. Her introduction to children's theatre came informally by way of one she set up in a studio guest house where her two boys and their friends produced a new play of their own creation each week. This experience, coupled with years of professional writing as a specialist in Public Relations led to a study of playwriting with Charlotte Chorpenning. Her published work includes an adaptation of

Dickens' A Christmas Carol, the beautifully styled Peter, Peter, Pumpkin Eater and a series of short plays, with Helen McKenna, for Child Life. Papa Pompino and the Prize-fighter won first prize in a Seattle Junior Programs National Playwriting Contest.

ALBERT O. MITCHELL (The Utah Trail) was born in the valley of the Little Salt Lake near the scene of the incidents of The Utah Trail. His home was at Parowan (in Ute language Pah-ruan, for evil water as the salt water was poisonous). In the time of the play, this was a mud-walled fort (the one mentioned in the play) and was the refuge of Frémont in his perilous trek in the winter of 1854. As a child, he saw the Indians often and loved to hear his father talk with them when they came on cold mornings to get warm or to beg for "prowa" (flour) or "pig-a-meat" (bacon). Summers were spent on his father's ranch, riding the trails over the Navajo mountain where Indians had left arrowheads scattered throughout the hills. His education, after high school, was at the University of Utah, the State University of Iowa and the University of Wisconsin, where he received a doctor's degree in speech and comparative literature in 1938. He has taught at the universities of Wisconsin, Minnesota and California, and is now professor of speech and director of the Young People's Theatre at the University of Utah. He was assigned to this work at the close of the war after service in the Pacific and Japan. His previous experiences with children's theatre were at the University of Minnesota and with Marguerite Blair in the organization of "Youtheatre" in Santa Barbara. Dr. Mitchell has arranged tours of the Young People's Theatre all over Utah and even as far as Omaha, Nebraska, in order to bring good theatre to "all the children of all the people." Perhaps the greatest reason for his interest in children's theatre can be found in a quote from one of his letters. "My greatest joy is my family (including five boys and two girls). For them and their friends, I write the plays. With them I take the stories we read and tell and make them come to life. It's fun! But they won't let me put in anything that's too sad, and they insist on our hanging the villain!" Other of his plays, written in this way, and produced for Young People's Theatre, include *The Prince and the Pauper, Jacob Hamblin—Friend of the Indians,* and *Mr. Popper's Penguins.*

NORA TULLY (MAC ALVAY) (*Titian*) was born in England and spent her childhood there and in Scotland. Coming to the United States with her family, she entered high school in Riverside, Illinois, where the accent was on progressive education. Soon she was bitten by the drama bug when she became involved with the writing and production of a school pageant on the early history of the town. Eager to explore the country when her preparation as a teacher was completed, she took assignments in northern Michigan, on an Indian reservation in Washington and in a steel mill district near Birmingham, Alabama. She has studied art at the Art Institute of Chicago, Northwestern University and the University of Missouri, and for a number of years was supervisor of art for the elementary schools in Hammond, Indiana. Her interest in art led to an exploration of theatre, with study at the universities of Indiana and Michigan, and the creation of an after-school theatre with junior high school students in Hammond. Since the war she and her husband have operated a book business with emphasis on children's literature. She acts as consultant to schools and libraries on children's books and has led teachers' workshops on children's literature and the use of creative dramatics in the language arts program. She founded and is currently directing the Michigan City, Indiana, Children's Theatre composed of a group of twelve- to eighteen-year-olds who play to younger audiences. She studied playwriting with Charlotte Chorpenning and the two collaborated on the popular *Elves and the Shoemaker* and *Flibbertygibbet*. Other plays include adaptations of *In Clean Hay* and *Beauty and the Beast* and a modern story of the Southwest, *Mystery in the Pueblo*. *Titian* had its first performance at the Goodman Theatre under Mrs. Chorpenning's direction, and has been published in England.